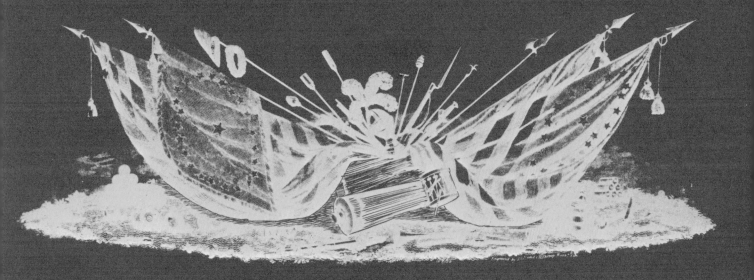

SMITHSONIAN INSTITUTION
United States National Museum Bulletin 269
Washington, D.C.
1969

UNITED STATES ARMY HEADGEAR TO 1854

Catalog of United States Army Uniforms in the
Collections of the Smithsonian Institution

VOLUME 1

EDGAR M. HOWELL
DONALD E. KLOSTER

Museum of History and Technology
Smithsonian Institution

Smithsonian Institution Press
City of Washington, 1969

Publications of the United States National Museum

The scholarly and scientific publications of the United States National Museum include two series, *Proceedings of the United States National Museum* and *United States National Museum Bulletin.*

In these series are published original articles and monographs dealing with the collections and work of its constituent museums—the Museum of Natural History and the Museum of History and Technology—setting forth newly acquired facts in the fields of Anthropology, Biology, History, Geology, and Technology. Copies of each publication are distributed to libraries, to cultural and scientific organizations, and to specialists and others interested in the various subjects.

The *Proceedings,* begun in 1878, are intended for the publication, in separate form, of shorter papers from the Museum of Natural History. These are gathered in volumes, octavo in size, with the publication date of each paper recorded in the table of contents of the volume.

In the *Bulletin* series, the first of which was issued in 1875, appear longer, separate publications consisting of monographs (occasionally in several parts) and volumes in which are collected works on related subjects. *Bulletins* are either octavo or quarto in size, depending on the needs of the presentation. Since 1902 papers relating to the botanical collections of the Museum have been published in the *Bulletin* series under the sub-series *Contributions from the United States National Herbarium.* Since 1959, in *Bulletins* titled "Contributions from the Museum of History and Technology," have been gathered shorter papers relating to the collections and research programs of that museum.

This work forms number 269 of the *Bulletin* series.

FRANK A. TAYLOR
Director, United States National Museum

For sale by the Superintendent of Documents, U.S. Government Printing Office
Washington, D.C. 20402 - Price $2.75

Contents

List of Illustrations

List of Abbreviations

A.G.	Adjutant General
AGO	Adjutant General's Office
CCF	Consolidated Correspondence File, Records of the Quartermaster General
CG of P	Commissary General of Purchases
Cloth. Bk.	Clothing Book, book of letters sent by the Quartermaster General re clothing
Cloth. Bur.	Clothing Bureau, War Department
Cloth. Estab.	Clothing Establishment, Schuylkill Arsenal, Philadelphia
Div. of Mil. Hist.	Division of Military History, Smithsonian Institution
G.O.	General Order
H.Q. of the Army	Headquarters of the Army
Masterson	An inventory of Philadelphia Depot records on file in the National Archives
LR	Letter Received
LS	Letter Sent
MS(S)	Manuscript(s)
MSK	Military Storekeeper
NA	National Archives, Washington, D.C.
n.d.	No Date
n.p.	No Pagination
n.v.	No Volume
O of AC & E	Office of Army Clothing and Equipage, Philadelphia Depot
OQMG	Office of the Quartermaster General
PO	Purveyor's Office, also termed Purveyor of Public Supplies
QM	Quartermaster
QMG	Quartermaster General
RG	Record Group, National Archives
USNM	United States National Museum
T.E.	Topographical Engineers

Preface

MILITARY DRESS HAS been a subject of much interest for more than a century in Great Britain and on the Continent where a large number of attractive military prints have been published and many scholarly works as well. Only in the last few decades has the United States shown a similar interest. Publications such as the *Military Collector & Historian* and its allied "Military Uniforms in America" have made a serious effort to fill this void, but no comprehensive study based on extant specimens has yet been made.

This volume is the first in a projected series on Regular Army dress based on the collections of the Museum of History and Technology of the Smithsonian Institution. Specifically it is a descriptive, critical, and documentary catalog of the headgear of the Regular Establishment through 1854. Succeeding volumes will cover headgear from 1854 to the present and uniforms and footwear. The complete series will embrace the period of the French and Indian War to the present day. It is hoped that these volumes will not only help fill a long neglected gap in our military history but will also reflect, to some extent the changing attitudes of the Army itself and the American people as a whole on matters of dress. Throughout our history the criteria of a sharp military appearance, sense of tradition, practicality, and economy have influenced in varying degree the form of dress of the military establishment.

Most students of military dress begin their work with a study of appropriate regulations, orders, etc., but soon run into the unenlightening and frustrating term "according to pattern," particularly in the case of enlisted men's uniforms. Officers' garb is generally described in greater detail, especially in earlier regulations, since officers purchased their uniforms from private firms that required accurate descriptions. Enlisted men's uniforms were procured or produced by the Army with the result that detailed descriptions were not deemed necessary since samples or pattern pieces were at hand.

The rich collections of the Smithsonian contain samples of most of the examples of enlisted men's headgear which have been imperfectly described in regulations and orders. While this volume is not intended to be a definitive history of military headgear for the period covered, it is designed to illustrate, describe, and document the specimens in the collections, furnish official descriptions when available, and provide pertinent correspondence on specific items, contemporary criticism, and reasons for adoption of new models.

All the specimens discussed in detail are from the national collections, most of them from the comprehensive War Department Collection, supplemented by the numerous biographical collections of the museum. Unmatched in scope and rarity, the War Department Collection is worthy of a note of its own. In general, the uniform elements of the collection date from 1832 and the headgear collection from some years earlier.

The Army established rigid standards for uniforms, headgear, and equipment early in its history. It furnished pattern pieces for those items which contractors were required to follow and which government inspectors used in checking completed work. This followed essentially the practice of the Ordnance Department. By 1813 it had become standard practice to maintain a collection of samples in the responsible offices of the War Department. Regulations, official correspondence, and contracts of the period used the phrase "according to pattern furnished' or "equal to the sealed patterns." Pattern pieces were stamped with an official seal of red wax and were retained after being superseded by newer patterns, along with stocks of older patterns that had been turned in, for use by uniform boards and the Secretary of War in considering proposed changes. During periods when the Army was considering changes in clothing items, officials in Washington (not wishing to rely on memory) would call for specimens from the Military Storekeeper in Philadelphia in order to examine previous styles, fabrics, and methods of manufacture. Thus the collection, coupled with field testing, was a valuable asset in research and development of new clothing and equipage.

Permanent status was given to the collection in the fall of 1865 when Brevet Major General Montgomery C. Meigs, the Quartermaster General of the Army, 1861–1882, directed the officer commanding at Schuylkill Arsenal in Philadelphia to establish at the Arsenal a museum of samples of uniform clothing and equipage in a fireproof building then about to be constructed. All "standard samples" were to be in locked display cases and all specimens were to be "properly labeled, catalogued, and protected." The project was not allowed to lag, indeed Meigs evidenced an active and continuing interest in it—both for historical and for research and development purposes—until his retirement. By 1869 the Museum had become well enough known to attract notice in the local press.

Beyond its research and development functions and its historical value, the museum served a broad public relations purpose. It was a point of interest to visitors to the Philadelphia metropolitan area. Portions of the collections were made available for public exhibit and were seen by hundreds of thousands of people at various national and international expositions beginning with the Centennial of 1876 and continuing into the early years of World War I. During the same period, a number of specimens were placed on long-term exhibit in the State-War-Navy Building in Washington.

In 1916, after the return of material loaned to the Panama-Pacific Exposition held in San Francisco the previous year, the entire collection at Philadelphia was placed in storage for want of space at the Arsenal. In 1919 it was turned over to the U.S. National Museum of the Smithsonian by the War Department. At the same time the specimens in the State-War-Navy Building were also transferred to the Smithsonian.

Over the years the collections had grown considerably: by 1913 there were 238 "lay figures" (uniforms on manikins) on exhibit. A few of these were patent reproductions, primarily of the Continental and War of 1812 periods for which authentic specimens did not exist in the Army. These reproductions, which have been isolated in the Smithsonian's collections and can be accounted for, will be the subject of a special note in a succeeding volume.

The biographical collections of the Smithsonian, although extensive but not to be compared with those from the War Department, are also of great importance. They contain many outstanding examples of officers' wear not included in the Philadelphia collection.

1854 has not been arbitrarily selected as a cut-off date; it happens in fact to mark the end of an era in headgear styling. In 1855 the broad-brimmed campaign hat was prescribed for the newly organized 1st and 2d Cavalry Regiments for both dress and fatigue and for the entire Army in March 1858. In November 1858 the "bummers" type forage cap was authorized and in the spring of 1859 all remaining stocks of the 1851–1854 cap were ordered issued for fatigue use.

During the months this study was in preparation, many people and institutions gave generously of their time and facilities. Foremost were the personnel of the Army-Air Force Branch of the National Archives, Mr. Elmer Parker, Mrs. Sara Jackson, Mr. Milton Chamberlain, and Mr. Sidney Haas. Their enthusiastic and continuing interest, their willingness to search and search again for an elusive document, and their sound advice based on years of experience with archival collections made this work possible. Also of great help has been the continuing aid of two experienced researchers working on projects of their own but never too busy to make note of or bring to the authors' attention material pertinent to this work: Mr. Detmar Finke of the Office, Chief of Military History, who reviewed the manuscript, and Mr. James Hutchins, Assistant Director, National Armed Forces Museum Advisory Board. Dr. Erna Risch, former chief, Historical Office, U.S. Army Materiel Command, also contributed much from her wide knowledge of the history of Army supply. Mrs. Grace Rogers Cooper, Curator, Division of Textiles, Museum of History and Technology, gave most generously of her time and her technical knowledge of fabrics. Thanks are also owing to Col. J. Duncan Campbell, the West Point Museum, the Coe Collection of the Yale University Library, and M. Knoedler and Co., New York, for illustrative material.

EDGAR M. HOWELL
Curator, Division of Military History
DONALD E. KLOSTER
Museum Specialist, Division of Military History

IN THE LATTER HALF OF THE 17TH CENTURY, the high-crowned, wide-brimmed, felted civilian headgear gradually became the typical European military hat. In time, the crown gradually became lower and the brim narrower, with one side looped up to permit free use of weapons and to give a rakish appearance. A plume of feathers and a cockade were often added and the whole was generally termed a cocked hat. By the 18th century the sides had become turned up to form the well-known three-cornered hat, sometimes called a tricorn, which predominated in most European armies for almost one hundred years.

The American settlers living in British colonies gen-erally followed the British military styles in such early uniforms as they had. In the main, the Continental Army wore the British-type tricon during the Revolu-tionary War.

An example of a tricorn of the Revolution is that worn by Colonel Jonathan Pettibone, 18th Connecti-cut Militia, in 1775 and 1776 (figs. 1–3). Civilian rather than military in general appearance, with its rather high crown and wide brim, it is in effect a transition between the earlier tricorn and the later military pattern with its neater and more compact design.

This specimen, of black wool felt with a small ad-

Figure 1.—Pettibone Tricorn, ca. 1776.

mixture of rabbit fur, measures 20¾ inches in diameter with a crown 5 inches high. The edges are bound with black silk ¾ of an inch wide and there are round 2½ inch black silk cockades on two sides. The rather deep sweatband is of glazed cotton fitted with a drawstring. Although the three sides are well stitched up,

of particular interest is the two-strand cotton string band about the crown indicating its quasi-civilian character as a plain round black hat worn with the sides down.

As the 18th century passed gradual changes were made: in British regiments the rear fold rising in contrast to the front corner, so that by 1800–1810 the hat had become two-cornered, or a bicorn, variously called throughout its further evolution during the next 40-odd years a "cocked" hat, a "chapeau," "chapeau bras," and "chapeau de bras." It was worn at right angles to the bridge of the nose, at a 45 degree angle, or directly fore and aft.[1]

Uniform regulations of the Army approved 30 January 1787 prescribed for officers and for enlisted men of the infantry and artillery "hats cocked," with "white trimmings" for the former, "yellow trimmings" for the latter, cockades "black leather, round, with points, four inches diameter . . . the feathers to rise six inches above the brim of the hat."[2] The feathers for the artillery were to be black with red tops, and those for the

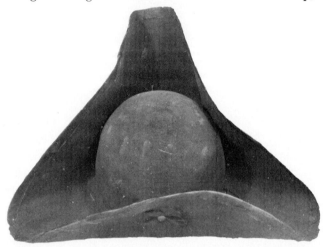

Figure 2.—Pettibone Tricorn, ca. 1776.

Figure 3.—Pettibone Tricorn, ca. 1776.

1st, 2nd, and 3rd Regiments of Infantry red, black, and white respectively. No authenticated specimen of this hat is known. Although the infantry dropped the chapeaux for the enlisted men by 1805 and for company grade officers by 1812, the foot artillery, officers and enlisted men, continued to wear them until 1812 and perhaps a little later. They were described as: "Hats, cocked or chapeaux de bras; black leather cockade with points 4 inches in diameter; a yellow button and eagle in the center; the button in uniform with the coat button, a white plume to project 6 inches above the hat." [3] The actual cut-off date is unknown. However, no contracts were let for this design after 1812. [4]

The uniform regulations issued 30 March 1800 described the headgear of a general staff officer as "a full cocked hat, with a yellow button, gold loop, and a black cockade, with a gold eagle in the center" and with a plume, the color of which depended on rank and as-

signment. No dimensions are given. The same regulations prescribed for infantry officers: "Hats, full cocked, with narrow black binding, fan or hind part eight inches broad—sides and corners six inches broad; Black Cockade of four inches diameter having a white eagle in the center, the cockade to rise an inch above the brim—loop and button black." [5]

No documented specimen conforming exactly to these specifications is known. That hat worn by Peter Gansevoort when brigadier general U.S.A. from 1809 to 1812, however, may be taken as typical of the period (figs. 4–5). [6] Made of heavy black beaver, the cock, or front, is 7¾ inches high and the fan, or rear, is 8½ inches; the corners, or distances from the sweatband to the points of the hat as seen, measure 4 inches; the whole is 16¼ inches point to point in a straight line. The edges are bound with black silk ribbon 1¾ inches wide, ⅞ of an inch showing to the outside, with an in-woven geometric pattern. Two diagonal stripes of

Figure 4.—Gansevoort Chapeau, ca. 1809–1812.

Figure 5.—Gansevoort Chapeau, fan down, ca. 1809–1812.

the same material frame the V-shaped "loop" of ⅜-inch gold bullion which terminates in a gold New York State "Excelsior" button.[7] The black silk cockade, 3½ inches in diameter, is of rather elaborate layered construction with a gold eagle of sophisticated design in the center. The 3-inch wide sweatband is decorated in gold both top and bottom, and the crown above it is lined with silk. There is a leather plume socket attached to the cock behind the cockade and loop, and there is evidence that both cock and fan were originally attached to the crown with black ribbon.

By 1812 the dimensions of the officers' chapeau had grown somewhat, the fan to be not less than 9½ inches nor more than 11 inches high.[8] In 1813 these had shrunk to not less than 6½ inches nor more than 9, point to point not less than 15 nor more than 17½, and to be without plumes.[9] This generally remained the pattern through the 1820s. The 1816, 1821, and 1825 regulations specify no change. No specimen conforming to these measurements which can be attributed to the Regular Army is in the national collections.

The 1832 uniform order brought a distinct change. Hats for general officers were to be

cocked, without binding; fan or back part eleven inches; the front or cock nine inches; each corner, six inches; black ribbons on the two front sides . . . . black silk cockade, six inches diameter; loop gold 11 inches long, ornamented with a spread silver eagle; gold rays emanating from the eagle 2½ inches computing from the center, terminating in 24 silver stars, plain or set with brilliants.

The plume for "A Major General Commanding in Chief" was to be "yellow swan feathers, drooping from an upright stem, feathered to the length of eight inches." The plume for all other major generals was to be "the same shape and materials, except that it will be black and white equally divided, the black below," that for brigadier generals to be similar with the colors "red and white, the white below." Tassels were to be "gold with worked hangers." Staff officers were authorized the same excepting the rays and stars, with the eagle gilt instead of silver; tassels were to be gold, with the plume the same as for general officers "with the distinction of colors to designate the Departments of the Staff." An exception was the Corps of Engineers for which a plume of three black ostrich feathers was prescribed. The hats could be "either opened or formed so as to shut like that hat which has heretofore been designated *chapeau de bras.*" [10] Field officers of the line were not authorized the chapeau for wear with their units, a circumstance which brought complaints from the field.[11] They were allowed, however, when not serving with troops, to "wear cocked hats of the same description as those prescribed for general staff officers, except that the loop [was to] be of black silk; the eagle yellow, the tassels to conform to the color of the button." [12]

Several specimens of this hat have survived, including those of Alexander Macomb (fig. 6), Commander-in-Chief of the Army, 1828–1841,[13] and Thomas Swords, an 1825 Military Academy graduate who served as a quartermaster for many years, and several others. All are of black beaver, are "open," or fitted to

Figure 6.—Macomb Chapeau, 1832 pattern.

the head, and conform closely to the regulations. The gold loop is interesting, in each case being made up of whorls of four strands of narrow gold braid and ornamented with horseshoes, lozenges, and buttons of gold braid, with the lower center button the appropriate uniform button of the wearer in each case. In two specimens the eagles on the loop do not carry a ribbon inscribed "E Pluribus Unum" in their beaks. The plume holders are set vertically behind the cockade. At each corner between the cock and fan is the "tassel—gold, with worked hangers," that is, an acorn of gold braid with strands of heavy braid attached. The cocks and fans, although stiffly vertical, are tied together with black ribbon. The sweatbands are of black patent leather fitted with drawstrings with the makers' labels on the silk crown lining.[14]

In 1838 the Bureau of Topographical Engineers was separated from the Corps of Engineers and established as an independent entity, the Corps of Topographical Engineers.[15] In May 1839 it was authorized its own uniform. The hat was identical to that prescribed for officers of the general staff in 1832 with the exception that the plume was to be black and the button of the Corps was to appear on the lower portion of the loop.[16]

General Order No. 7, Headquarters of the Army, 18 February 1840, which authorized a number of changes in the uniform of the Corps of Engineers, described the hat: "same as for General Officers, except that the corners are to be four and a half inches long, instead of six" and the loop to be a "plain gold strap, two inches wide, raised embroidered edges; ornamented with gilt spread eagle and scroll." The plume remained three black ostrich feathers. The specimen illustrated (fig. 7) belonged to George B. McClellan when a lieutenant of engineers and conforms quite precisely, with the exception of the eagle on the strap, to both the specifications as written and the approved drawings submitted by the Corps (fig. 8).[17] One particular difference between this hat and the others is the plume holder, which is set on the crown at such a slant as to indicate clearly that the hat was intended to be worn with the loop to the left. The silk lining of the crown carries the label of the maker, M. C. St. John of 118 Broadway, New York City.

The 1851 uniform regulations, which provided for quite a drastic change in almost all elements of the Army's dress, did not prescribe a chapeau. As a concession to the ranking officers of the service, however, general officers and colonels holding the brevet rank of general were allowed to wear their chapeaux on ceremonial occasions and when not serving with troops.[18] A chapeau was reauthorized in 1858 for general wear, and this time for field officers as well as those of the general staff. In December 1859 a new style chapeau came into being, the 1858 order being modified "to permit all officers of the General Staff, and Staff Corps, to wear, at their option, a light French chapeau, either stiff crown or flat . . . officers below the rank of Field Officers to wear but two feathers." [19]

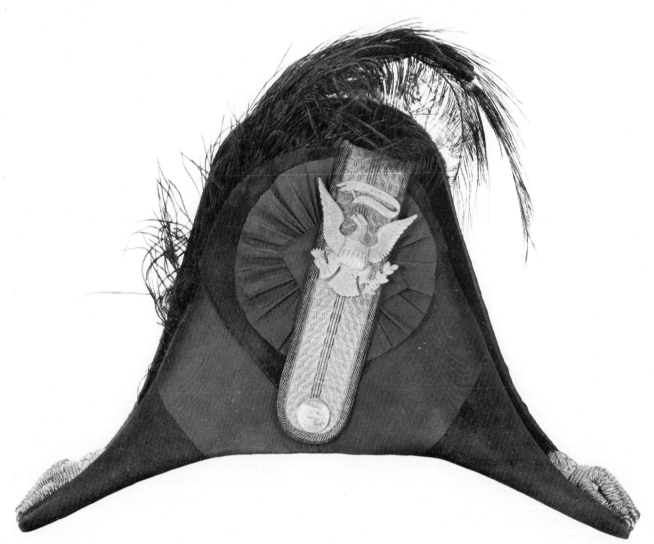

Figure 7.—McClellan Chapeau, 1840 pattern.

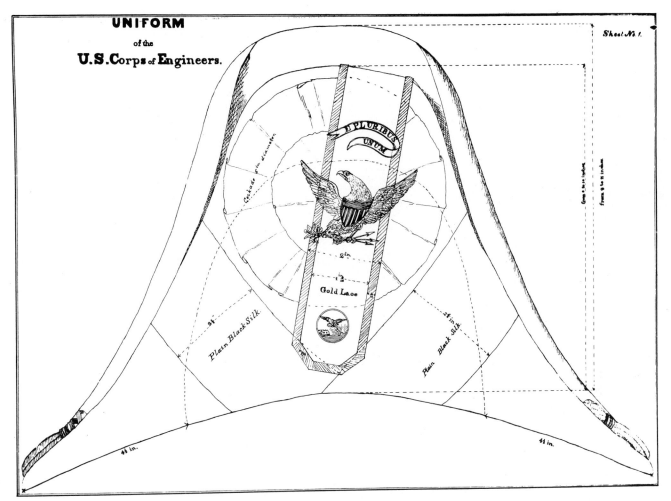

Figure 8.—Chapeau for Corps of Engineers, 1840. Official drawing. National Archives.

NOTES

[1] See W. Y. Carman, *British Military Uniforms from Contemporary Pictures* (London, 1957); Cecil C. P. Lawson, *A History of the Uniforms of the British Army*, 3 vols. (London 1940, 1941, 1961); and R. M. Barnes, *A History of the Regiments & Uniforms of the British Army* (London, n.d.) for many illustrations of the evolution of the chapeau.

[2] Untitled MS, "War Office, Dec. 26th 1786," in Castle Island Orderly Book, 13 Jan.-20 Apr. 1787, Post Revolutionary War Records, vol. 8, Adjutant General's Records, Record Group 94 (hereinafter cited as RG 94), National Archives (hereinafter cited as NA).

[3] G.O., Southern Dept., Headquarters, Charleston, 24 Jan. 1813, in U.S. Army Command, Post Rev. War Records, vol. 39, RG 94, NA. See also H. Charles McBarron, Jr., and John R. Elting, "3rd Regiment, United States Artillery, 1812," *Military Collector & Historian* (Summer 1964), vol. 16, no. 2, p. 48. The 2nd and 3rd Artillery Regiments, authorized in January 1812, possibly wore the chapeau for a short time. See Sec. of War Wm. Eustis to Callender Irvine, Commissary General of Purchases, 31 Aug. 1812. Letters sent (hereinafter cited as LS), Records of the Secretary of War, RG 107 (hereinafter cited as RG 107), NA.

[4] See appendix.

[5] G.O., Headquarters, Fort Adams [Mississippi], 30 Mar. 1800, G.O., U.S. Army, RG 94. These may have been only provisional regulations, the Army possibly reverting to the 1797 regulations in 1801.

[6] During the period of Gansevoort's commission there were no specific regulations for general officers' dress.

[7] The presence of this particular button on the hat is not explained, but it is probably a holdover from Gansevoort's service as a New York Militia officer. Gansevoort, a native New Yorker, served in both the Continental Army and the New York State Militia during the Revolution. In 1802 he was appointed Military Agent Northern Dept. and in 1809 Brigadier General, U.S.A. Judging by the technique of manufacture used, the button probably dates no earlier than about 1800.

[8] G.O., Headquarters, Charleston, 24 Jan. 1813, op. cit.

[9] "Changes in the Uniform of the Army . . . .," *American State Papers, Military Affairs* (Washington, 1832), vol. 1, pp. 433–434.

[10] *Dress of the General Staff and Regimental Officers of the Army of the United States,* Adjutant General's Office, Washington, 31 May 1832, Order No. 50, Adjutant General's Office, Headquarters of the Army (hereinafter cited as H.Q. of the Army), Washington, 11 June 1832. For the colors of the plumes of the staff departments, see *ibid.*

[11] Lt. Col. Daniel Baker, 6th Inf., to Major John Garland, Clothing Bureau, 7 Jan. 1833, Clothing Bureau (hereinafter cited as Cloth. Bur.) LR, filed with Quartermaster General Records, Record Group 92 (hereinafter cited as RG 92), NA. In 1832 the Secretary of War established the Clothing Bureau as a direct appendage of the War Department, its head reporting directly to and advising the Secretary on all problems connected with the clothing of the Army.

[12] *Dress of the General Staff and Regimental Officers* . . ., op. cit.

[13] Unaccountably, the plume on Macomb's hat is white rather than the prescribed yellow.

[14] The makers of the specimens examined were Wm. H. Horstmann & Sons and J. H. Wilson, both of Philadelphia.

[15] John F. Callan, *The Military Laws of the United States* . . . (Philadelphia, 1863), pp. 342–343.

[16] Asst. Adj. Gen. L. Thomas to Col. J. J. Abert, Commanding Corps of Topographical Engineers, 7 May 1839, LS, Topographical Bureau, RG 77, NA.

[17] Commissary General of Purchases (hereinafter cited as CG of P), LR, tray 69, RG 92, NA.

[18] G.O. 31, H.Q. of the Army, 12 June 1851, NA. See especially paragraph 213.

[19] General Orders No. 3, Adjutant General's Office, War Department, Washington (hereinafter cited as G.O. War Dept.), 24 Mar. 1858; G.O. 27, War Dept., 22 Dec. 1859, NA.

☆LIGHT DRAGOON HELMET, WAR OF 1812 PERIOD☆

Gᴇɴᴇʀᴀʟ ᴏʀᴅᴇʀꜱ, Headquarters, Fort Adams, Mississippi, dated 30 March 1800 prescribed: "For the Corps of Cavalry . . . . a helmet of leather crowned with black horse hair, and having a brass front, with a mounted Dragoon in the Act of Charging . . . . The helmets of the officers distinguished by green plumes." [20] This "Corps of Calvary" comprised the light dragoons authorized in 1796 when the Legion—as the U.S. Army was known from 1792 to 1796—went out of existence. It continued on the rolls until the reduction of the Army in 1802. [21]

When the Army was increased in 1808 as a result of the Chesapeake-Leopard affair, a regiment of light dragoons was authorized along with other units. [22] Their headgear is described as "leather Caps or Helmets, with blue Feathers, tipt with White . . . . the feathers of privates not to exceed ten inches in length." [23] A strip of bearskin was to be attached to the top with the letters "USLD" in brass affixed to the front to indicate branch of service, the entire helmet to cost $2.50. [24] These brass letters were changed to "white metal" in keeping with the other metal trimmings of the corps. [25] No authenticated specimens of this helmet are known to have survived. A few years later a new helmet form with a cap plate rather than letters was authorized for dragoons, for a contract dated 16 October 1812 for dragoon caps included the statement "with plates in front per pattern." In fact, as early as March 1813 the Military Storekeeper at Philadelphia reported 1238 dragoon caps of the "new Pattern" on hand and 37 of the old. [26] These cap plates were produced by George Armitage of Philadelphia. [27]

The lack of a precise description of this helmet or plate, together with other factors, makes its design, at least in 1812 and 1813, somewhat uncertain and indicates that it went through one or more modifications before arriving at the design illustrated (figs. 9–11).

The 1812 regulation prescribes merely a "Helmet, according to pattern, blue feather with white top, feather 9 inches long." [28]

Although many regulations of this period deal only with officers' uniforms, the feather was definitely used on the enlisted men's helmet as well. Many entries of materiel received and issued to the dragoons specifically mention the feather in connection with the helmet, and the term dragoon feather is clearly pointed out to distinguish it from feathers used by other corps of the Army. [29] In addition to this feather, the enlisted dragoons were also issued cockades and eagles for their helmets. [30] A search of contracts and issues during the entire period 1812–1815 did not reveal any mention of a special cockade or eagle for the dragoons, so it must be assumed that they were using the same type issued to other branches of the Army.

This very specific mention of the use of feathers, cockades, and eagles for the dragoon helmet poses a problem in relation to the examples in the United States National Museum. There is no place where these feathers could have been mounted on these helmets, unless of course they were used in place of the white horsehair, nor is there any physical evidence that a cockade and eagle was ever affixed to any of them. The only solution is that these examples represent a second or even a third type or modification. In any case, all of the helmets from 1808 on were apparently of leather, as contracts dating back that far make frequent mention of dragoon caps of leather and all of the contractors are known to have been saddlers or manufacturers of leather equipment.

The authenticity of the United States National Museum specimens as items of regular army issue as opposed to militia is difficult to doubt, despite the lack of an official detailed description. The undersurfaces of the visors, except those samples on which the leather

Figure 9.—Light Dragoon Helmet, ca. **1814**

Figure 10.—Light Dragoon Helmet, ca. **1814**.

Figure 11.—Light Dragoon Helmet, ca. 1814.

"jacking" has flaked off, bear the marks "H. Cressman" and "G^{V}F." Henry Cressman delivered 246
dragoon "caps" to the Military Storekeeper in Philadelphia during 1814 and 1815, in addition to several
thousand leather infantry caps.[31] The initials "G^{V}F,"
in cloverleaf form, refer to one George Flomerfelt who
was United States inspector of leather goods at the
Schuylkill Arsenal in Philadelphia from late 1813 until
at least April 1816.[32] His initials as a U.S. inspector

would not have appeared on militia helmets. The white
horsehair crest as opposed to the feather, cockade, and
eagle mentioned in regulations has never been accounted for in any order or instruction located, but
internal correspondence of the Commissary General of
Purchases' office does make several mentions of this
horsehair. In July 1814 the Commissary General instructed Flomerfelt to procure 50 to 100 pounds of
"long white horsehair" and in July and August of the

12

same year Henry Cressman and Abraham P. Foering, both of whom supplied dragoon helmets to the Army in 1814, were issued 50 and 33 pounds respectively of horsehair.[33] No other type of enlisted man's headgear required any sort of horsehair crest in 1814, so it must be assumed that this hair was for the crests on the type of helmet illustrated (figs. 9–11). These specimens came to the National Museum from the Quartermaster Clothing Museum at Schuylkill Arsenal—which was never a repository for militia material in bulk—and are of a durable material not subject to insect or casual damage. While other forms of headgear could have been and were issued to the Army after the end of the war, the dragoons were disbanded in 1815 and not reconstituted until 1833.[34] An inventory of stores on hand in February 1815 showed 88 dragoon caps still in stock, and in May 1815 Cressman, apparently completing an earlier contract, delivered an additional 122.[35]

The crested helmet, whether of leather or metal, initially designed for horse units to protect the head against saber strokes, was known in both Europe and America well before the opening of the 19th century and became traditional for dress wear in many mounted organizations after 1800.[36] This cap, strongly made of jacked leather,[37] is of basic two-piece construction with each half running up to form one side of the comb, and not of the so-called "jockey cap" style which had the comb added.[38] The comb rises 3 inches above the cap proper at its highest point and tapers to the rear, the overall height of the helmet being 9 inches at the peak. The comb is bound with white metal strips riveted together through the leather with a white horsehair crest rising from the center. This crest, which falls to the side, measures 18 inches at its greatest length. The horizontal and vertical metal strips binding the sides of the cap are wired on. The convex visor, of the same material as the cap, is 3 inches at its widest point and measures 10 inches from side to side. The side band is of thin leather tapering from 2¼ inches at the rear to 1 inch in front. A patent leather sweatband is welted to the outside of the cap and turned under, with canvas fitted with a drawstring attached above. The chin scales, attached to the sides of the cap with pewter buttons, are of hand-cut white metal wired to welted leather straps, meeting in the center of the visor and held in place there by another pewter button. The placement of the straps and their length indicate that they would not meet under the chin of

the wearer and were only decorative The cap plate, of medium thickness pewter, carries the "mounted dragoon in the act of charging" as prescribed in the 1800 regulations and is attached with waxed linen thread. On the underside of the visor is stamped the maker's name, "H. Cressman," and the inspector's initials, "GᵛF," in a cloverleaf form.

NOTES

[20] G.O. U.S. Army, RG 94, NA.

[21] There were only two troops of dragoons during this period. In 1798 six additional troops were authorized but never raised.

[22] Callan, op. cit., pp. 200–201.

[23] Notice signed by Sec. of War Henry Dearborn dated 21 May 1808, reproduced in James E. Hicks, *United States Ordnance,* vol. 2, *Ordnance Correspondence* (Mt. Vernon, N.Y., 1940), p. 21. The terms helmet and cap were used interchangeably at this time. While regulations normally used helmet, official correspondence tended to prefer cap. In this section helmet will be used to designate the style more clearly.

[24] Tench Coxe, Purveyor of Public Supplies, to Jonathan Lukens (a contractor), 1 July 1808, Purveyor's Office, LS, RG 92, NA; J. Duncan Campbell and Edgar M. Howell, *American Military Insignia, 1800–1851,* U.S. National Museum Bulletin 235 (Washington, 1963), p. 11. The bear skin was substituted for originally prescribed leopard skin.

[25] Col. James Burn, C.O. 2d Regiment of Dragoons (authorized 11 Jan. 1812) to Sec. of War William Eustis, 8 July 1812, LR, Sec. of War, RG 107, NA; B. Mifflin, Dep. Comm. Gen. of Purchases at Boston, to Sec. of War, 9 July 1812, LR, RG 107, NA; Campbell and Howell, op. cit., p. 11.

[26] Campbell and Howell, op. cit., p. 11; Geo. Ingels, Military Storekeeper (hereinafter cited as MSK), Philadelphia, to Irvine, 10 Mar. 1813, Letter Book, CG of P, RG 92, NA: Irvine to Amasa Stetson, Deputy Quartermaster, 31 Mar. 1813, LS, CG of P, RG 92; Contract with Mathew Lyons, Philadelphia, 16 Oct. 1812, Consolidated Correspondence File (hereinafter cited as CCF) under Mathew Lyons, RG 92, NA.

[27] Irvine to Amasa Stetson, 31 Mar. 1813, LS, CG of P, RG 92, NA; MSK "Blotter," entries for 30 Mar. and 31 Mar. 1813, 9 Mar. and 30 Mar. 1814, RG 92, NA. Armitage was a prime supplier of these plates. He is listed in the Philadelphia directories as a "silverplater" and "military ornament maker," and produced many of the finely designed and struck insignia and buttons worn by the Army from 1802 to ca. 1825. See Campbell and Howell, op. cit., pp. 12–23.

[28] G.O., 24 Jan. 1813, op. cit.; *Military Laws, and Rules and Regulations for the Army of the United States* (Washington City: Roger Chew Weightman, Dec. 1814), pp. 105–110.

[29] MSK "Blotter" and "Journal" for 1812–1814, RG 92, NA; M. J. Littleboys was one of the contractors that

supplied these feathers at 35 cents each. See "Blotter" entry, 8 Oct. 1812.

[30] MSK "Blotter" entry, 8 Oct. 1812, dealing with an issue of dragoon clothing to Capt. Cummings in Pittsburgh, RG 92, NA, and numerous other issues in this "Blotter" and its succeeding "Journal" through an 8 Nov. 1814 issue to Col. Burn, 2nd Light Dragoons.

[31] MSK "Blotter" and "Journal" entries, 22 Aug. 1814, 11 Nov. 1814, and 10 May 1815.

[32] Irvine to Flomerfelt, 2 Dec. 1813, 8 Apr. 1816, CG of P, LS, RG 92, NA.

[33] Irvine to Flomerfelt, 22 July 1814, CG of P, LS; MSK "Journal" entries, 30 July and 2 Aug. 1814—all RG 92, NA.

[34] G.O. Adjutant and Inspector General's Office, 17 May 1815, RG 94, NA; Irvine to Acting Sec. of War, 29 July 1817, CG of P, LS, RG 92, NA.

[35] MSK "Journal" entry, 10 May 1815, RG 92, NA.

[36] See Waverly P. Lewis, *U.S. Military Headgear, 1770–1880* (Devon, Conn., 1960), and H. C. B. Rogers, *The Mounted Troops of the British Army, 1066–1945* (London, 1959), only two of many excellent references on the subject for photos of actual specimens and contemporary illustrations of such caps.

[37] Leather that has been hardened or reinforced in any one of a number of methods, in this case with a black lacquer.

[38] See Lewis, op. cit., p. 10.

A BLACK CYLINDRICAL CAP of felt or beaver was prescribed in late 1811 for infantry platoon officers and enlisted personnel: 6⅞ to 7¼ inches in height with a visor of 2½ inches, with cords and tassels, and a front plate "with the eagle, the number of the regiment and designation of the service." [39] This cap apparently was modeled on that adopted by the foot troops of the British Army about 1800 and also worn by units of the French Army. The British model was of japanned leather rather than felt. [40] No specimen of the American model is known to exist.

On 23 January 1813 the Secretary of War approved a new pattern infantry cap that had been submitted to his office for examination. [41] This was in response to a recommendation made by the Commissary General of Purchases, Callender Irvine, the previous December. Irvine, who had never liked the wool felt caps, had stated at that time:

> For the men of the Light Artillery, Infantry, Artillery and Rifle Regiments, I propose to furnish Leather Caps in lieu of Felt Caps, the former being preferable as to appearance, comfort, durability and on the score of economy, the leather cap will cost $1. The Felt Cap costs 87½ Cts. the former will last three to four years with decency, under any circumstances two years, the latter but one year and will not look decent half that time, the first wetting injures its good appearance. . . . [42]

In February 1813 Irvine informed his deputy commissaries of the intention to furnish the Army with leather caps "as soon as those on hand and contracted for are issued." [43] During the same month he called in hat manufacturers to examine the new pattern leather infantry cap, [44] and during March and April let contracts for this piece of headgear at an average cost of $1.79. [45]

Unfortunately the approval of this cap contains no detailed description, and the first uniform regulation which mentions it, that of 1 May 1813, states only: "Leather caps will be substituted for felt, and worsted or cotton pompons for feathers." [46] Postwar regulations add further clarity as to the trimmings: "Cap, for the non-commissioned officers and privates of all corps, the same as that worn by the infantry, with white pompons, black cockades, and yellow cockade eagles; the other ornaments of the cap to correspond with the trimmings of the corps." [47] The other ornaments included a band and tassel as well as a cap plate. [48] Subsequent official correspondence adds further detail. The cap was lined, had a front piece to rise 2⅝ inches above the crown, and was equipped with rings and buttons, one on either side of the cap, to secure the bands and tassels. [49] In 1816 the dimensions in inches of a cap of this type in actual use are finally given: "height of back–7½, height of front above crown–2, diameter of top–7, diameter of bottom–7¾. Flaps on the back,

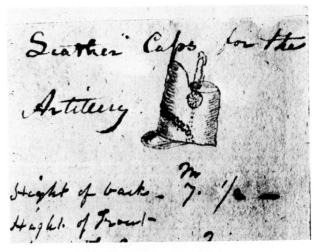

Figure 12.—Infantry Cap, 1813–1821. Contemporary drawing. National Archives.

turned inside. Top arched. Front of the cap supported by the arch of the top, which slopes down from its top." [50]

There were numerous variations in these caps between 1813 and 1821, partially owing to the large number of different contractors who made them during the period and partially to the minor changes authorized by the Secretary of War in his original letter of approval in which he stated: "with such improvements as experience may suggest." [51] Among others these variations included the method of attaching the front to the crown, painting the edge of the "front piece" white, a molding of blocked tin around the cap, and the height of the "front piece" above the crown. [52]

This cap followed a pattern adopted by the British in 1812. In that year they replaced their leather "stovepipe" with a new shako of felt, still cylindrical but with the body shortened and a false front added to give the ilusion of height. This new type was generally termed the "Waterloo" after 1815. [53] It is interesting to note that the United States adopted a British pattern even though at war with them at the time.

Two specimens of this pattern cap which can be ascribed to the Regular Establishment with fair degree of certainty have been examined and are almost identical in construction and appearance, although differing somewhat in height. Both are of basic three-piece construction, that is cylinder, visor, and crown, well-made throughout, and painted black. The one in the national collections (figs. 13–15) is believed possibly to have been an officer's cap in view of the very stylish, albeit non-regulation, front plate which gives evidence of being original. [54] Not quite cylindrical, the cap measures $6\frac{1}{2}$ inches in diameter at the top and $7\frac{1}{2}$ in the base. Overall height with the false front is $9\frac{1}{2}$ inches with the height to the seam $6\frac{1}{2}$. [55] The visor measures 2 inches at its widest point, and is 9 inches from side to side. Its underside is painted green. The vertical seam of the cylinder is on the left and is covered by a leather strip $\frac{7}{8}$ of an inch wide. Perforations around the top of this strip indicate that the prescribed leather cockade and pompon were once attached at that point. Although no examples of the plaited cord are known, a contemporary drawing (fig. 16) [56] indicates that it ran diagonally across the front of the cap from upper right to lower left and was attached to two silver-on-copper semi-spherical buttons present on this specimen.

Figure 13.—Infantry Cap, 1813–1821.

Figure 14.—Infantry Cap, 1813–1821.

16

Figure 15.—Infantry Cap, 1813–1821.

Figure 16. —Infantry Cap, 1813–1821. Detail from "Pawnee Council" by S. Seymour. Coe Collection, Yale University Library.

There are no "rings" as called for. The tassels were attached to the right-hand or upper button. The base of the cap is trimmed with three strands of twisted silver-on-copper wire running across the visor and held in place by two small silvered buttons. There was no chin strap. The sweatband is of patent leather and has an upper band of canvas attached fitted with a drawstring. The rear of the cap comes to a slight V over the nape of the neck. There is no evidence that the specimen was ever fitted with the folded "flap" in the rear known on others of this type. There is no maker's name or inspector's initials.[57]

As predicted by Callender Irvine at the time of its adoption, this cap was a success from the point of view of durability, for only two were issued each soldier during his five-year enlistment.[58] A further indication of its utility and popularity is the fact that in September of 1816 it was prescribed for enlisted men of all branches of the service.[59]

NOTES

[39] Tench Coxe, Purveyor of Public Supplies, to Lt. John R (illegible), 2d Inf., N.Y., 21 Feb. 1812, Purveyor's Office (hereinafter cited PO), LS; Coxe to Arch. B. Wil-

liams, 28 Feb. 1812, PO, LS; circular letter, Coxe to all his deputy purveyors, 24 Mar. 1812, PO, LS; all RG 92, NA; G.O., 24 Jan. 1813, op. cit., describes the front plate as an "oblong silver plate . . . bearing the name of the corps and number of the regiment."

[40] W. Y. Carman, *British Military Uniforms from Contemporary Pictures* (London, 1957), p. 111.

[41] Sec. of War John Armstrong to Irvine, 23 Jan. 1813, LS, Military Affairs vol. 6, RG 107, NA.

[42] Irvine to Sec. of War, 26 Dec. 1812, CG of P, LS, RG 92, NA.

[43] Irvine to Amasa Stetson, Boston, 18 Feb. 1813, CG of P, LS, RG 92, NA.

[44] Irvine to Messrs. Martin, Primrose, Lyons, Lukens, Kerr, and Walker, 18 Feb. 1813, CG of P, LS, RG 92, NA.

[45] Sec. War to Senate, 28 March 1814, Legislative Records Branch, Records of U.S. Senate, RG 46, NA.

[46] *American State Papers, Military Affairs,* op. cit., vol. 1, pp. 433–434.

[47] *Military Laws, Rules and Regulations for the Army of the United States, Adjutant and Inspector General's Office, September 1816* (E. de Krafft, n.d.), p. 131.

[48] *Articles of War, Military Laws and Rules and Regulations for the Army of the United States, Adjutant and Inspector General's Office, September, 1816, revised 1817*

(E. de Krafft, n.d.). For illustration and description of the cap plate, see Campbell and Howell, op cit., pp. 12–15.

[49] George Flomerfelt, U.S. Inspector of Leather Goods, U.S. Arsenal, 17 Mar. 1814, to unlisted addressee, CCF (Flomerfelt), RG 92, NA. This letter deals with Flomerfelt's inspection of caps produced in 1813 as compared with the pattern cap of that year. See also contract with Violet Primrose, 10 Apr. 1813, in Sec. of War to Senate, 28 Mar. 1814, Legislative Records Branch, Records of the U.S. Senate, RG 46, NA.

[50] Quoted in Hugh Charles McBarron, Jr., "American Military Dress in the War of 1812—III Regular Infantry," *Journal of the American Military Institute,* (Fall 1940) vol. 4, no. 3, p. 194. These measurements and the accompanying sketch (fig. 12) were found among the papers of the Commissary General of Purchases and photostated by Detmar Finke, Office, Chief of Military History, many years ago when the files were stored at Fort Myer, Va. They have not been located since the transfer of the files to the National Archives.

[51] Sec. of War to Irvine, 23 Jan. 1813, LS, Military Affairs vol. 6, RG 107, NA.

[52] McBarron, "American Military Dress in the War of 1812," op. cit.; contract with Violet Primrose, 10 Apr. 1813; contract with Samuel Dallam, 20 Mar. 1813—both in Sec. of War to Senate, 28 Mar. 1814, Legislative Records Branch, Records of U.S. Senate, RG 46, NA.

[53] R. M. Barnes, *A History of the Regiments and Uniforms of the British Army* (London, n.d.) p. 118; Richard J. Koke, "The Britons Who Fought on the Canadian Frontier, Uniforms of the War of 1812," *New-York Historical Society Quarterly* (April 1961), vol. 45, no. 2, pp. 141–194; Alex R. Cattley, "The British Infantry Shako," *Journal of the Society for Army Historical Research* (Winter 1936), vol. 15, no. 60, pp. 188–208. Generally known as the Waterloo shako in Britain, it has also been called the Wellington and Belgic. It was worn in somewhat different form by Portugese troops ca. 1805 and by the infantry of the King's German Legion late in the Napoleonic Wars. In America it has often been termed the "tombstone."

[54] Campbell and Howell, op. cit., pp. 16–17.

[55] These measurements, with minor variations, are in line with those quoted in a contemporary letter to Irvine. See McBarron, "American Military Dress in the War of 1812," op. cit., p. 194. The other specimen examined is somewhat lower, being 8 inches high overall and 5¾ to the seam.

[56] Detail from watercolor "Pawnee Council" by S. Seymour, Coe Coll., Yale Univ. Lib. Seymour painted this in 1819 while accompanying the Long Expedition.

[57] The other cap, in the collection of J. Duncan Campbell, has "R. Redfern" on a yellow paper label pasted in the crown. This was Robert Redfern, of 403 High St., Philadelphia, who received his first contract for this type of cap in 1819. For makers of this cap see appendix.

[58] *Articles of War . . . Revised 1817,* op. cit., p. 87.

[59] *Military Laws . . . September 1816,* op. cit., p. 131.

☆BELL CROWN CAP, 1821–1832☆

DURING THE WAR OF 1812, while the infantry was wearing the "stovepipe" and the "Wellington" or "tombstone" caps, the light and foot artillery and the rifle regiments were wearing the Continental "yeoman crown" cap, with the top wider than the base,[60] authorized in 1813. The "bell crown"—like the yeoman crown with the top wider than the base but with distinctly concave sides—prescribed in the 1821 uniform regulations was a direct reflection of European modes, first the Russians, then the Prussians, and by 1830 almost every European army except the French having adopted it.[61] First authorized in April 1820,[62] the 1821 Uniform Regulations describe the "bell crown" as follows:

Caps of company officers will be of leather; bell crown; gilt scales; yellow eagle, in front, three inches between the tips of the wings, with the number of the regiment cut in the shield; black leather cockade, one and a half inch in diameter, having a small yellow button in the centre, with an eagle impressed on it. Those of the enlisted men will be of leather, and of the same form as those prescribed for officers; brass scales.

Chapeau de bras will be worn by all officers in uniform, whether of the line or the staff, except company officers. Caps will be worn by all company officers when on duty with their companies, and by all enlisted men.

  .   .   .   .   .   .

The company officers of artillery will wear yellow pompons five inches in length; those of the light artillery to be white, with red tops. The officers of infantry will wear similar pompons, except in colour, which shall be white; those of the light infantry companies to be yellow. The officers of rifle companies will wear like pompons, except in colour, which shall be green.

Yellow worsted pompons, five inches in length, will be worn by the enlisted men of the artillery; those of the light artillery to be white, with red tops. The enlisted men of the infantry will wear similar pompons, except in colour, which shall be white; those of the light infantry companies to be yellow. The enlisted men of the rifle companies will wear like pompons, except in colour, which shall be green.

Pompons will be worn in front of the cap.

[Tassels] of the officers of the artillery and rifle companies will be of gold cord and bullion. Those of the officers of infantry will be of silver cord and bullion.

Those of the enlisted men of artillery will be of yellow worsted; those of the enlisted men of infantry will be of white worsted; and those of the enlisted men of the rifle corps will be of green worsted.[63]

Although these regulations prescribed brass rather than the traditional "white metal" for the scales and plate on the infantry cap, the latter was adopted before the new pattern was issued. Irvine, in recommending the change to the Secretary of War several months after the regulations were issued, stated that at the time of the adoption of the new pattern no suitable white metal was available, but it could now be obtained in a form both cheap and durable and capable of taking a high polish.[64] The suggestion was approved in January 1822 and instructions issued that thereafter all infantry cap trimmings were to be of white metal.[65] Despite this order, the change, oddly enough, was not included in the regulations issued in 1825. Still, there is no doubt that it was made, for cost of clothing lists for several years during the 1820s list artillery and infantry cap scales separately and at slightly different prices, and in 1830 Robert Dingee, a New York supplier, writes to Irvine of making white cap scales. This is further substantiated by the excavation of scales of pewter, or "white metal," at Fort Atkinson, Nebraska, where the regular infantry served from 1819 to 1827, and where militia units are not known to have been stationed.[66]

Although a number of bell crown caps of the general period 1820–1835 are in existence, the cap illustrated (figs. 17–19) is one of only two of the many examined which do not carry typical militia embellishment and which generally conform to regulations. Well made of black-painted leather, the specimen is 6 inches high measured at the side, the top 10 inches in diameter, visor 2 inches wide and nearly vertical.[67] The rear of the cap is slightly pointed over the nape of the neck and has a 1 inch strip of leather running around it from the terminals of the visor. The leather cockade at the top of the front is the regulation 1½ inches and carries the prescribed line eagle button, with the letter "A" on the shield.[68] The eagle front plate conforms to regulations.[69] Both eagle and button appear to be original to the cap. The "band," actually a plaited cord, is also believed to be original. The chin scales and tassel are missing. The means of attachment for the scales—plain brass buttons with their shanks to the outside of the cap—remain in place. In the center of the visor at its base is a small, two-pronged brass piece on which the scales rested. The sweatband is of patent leather and has an upper band of canvas fitted with drawstrings. The cap carries no maker's label and no inspector's mark. Complete with the oil cloth or painted linen cover issued with it, pompon, band and tassel, cockade and eagle, and cap plate, it cost $3.01, the cap alone $1.50, in contrast to the 1813–1821 model priced at $1.95 in 1817.[70] Officers' caps of the new

pattern were furnished complete by George Armitage at a cost of $8.50.[71] The entire army was equipped with this cap by early 1823 when the old pattern was turned in.[72]

The other specimen examined, in the collections of the Historical Society of Old Newbury, Newburyport, Massachusetts, is almost identical to that illustrated, and carries very similar "bands" to both front and rear as well as the prescribed brass chin scales. It also carries in the crown the maker's label, "H. Cressman, 136 No. Eighth St. Phila."

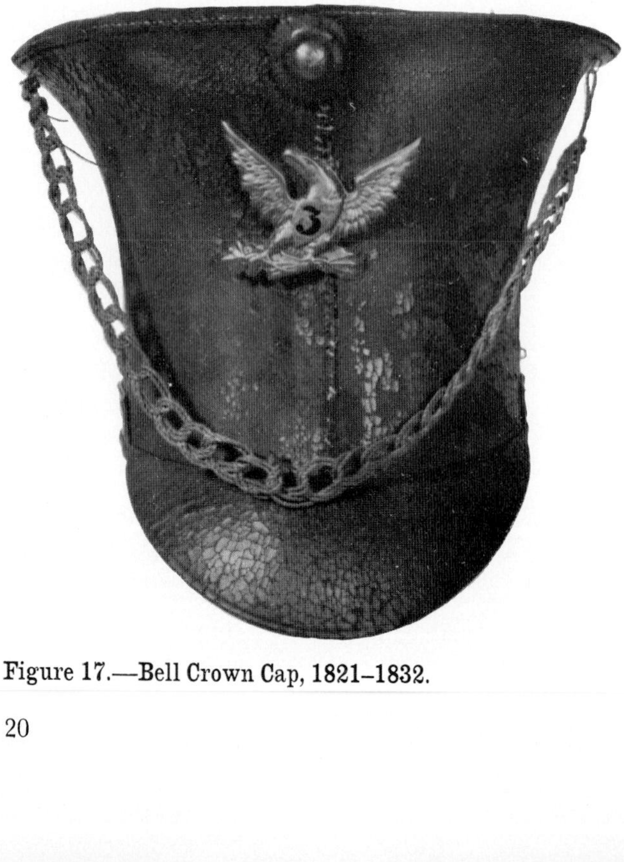

Figure 18.—Bell Crown Cap, 1821–1832.

Figure 17.—Bell Crown Cap, 1821–1832.

Figure 19.—Bell Crown Cap, 1821–1832.

20

These caps, with plate, scales, and oil cloth cover were issued at the rate of one per each five year enlistment. As further evidence of its durability, it should be noticed that the cap with plate and scales was considered government property, not part of the soldier's clothing allowance, and was to be turned in at the expiration of his term of service.[73]

NOTES

[60] G.O. 24 Jan. 1813, op. cit.; Tench Coxe, Purveyor of Public Supplies, to Sec. of War William Eustis, 8 Mar. 1812, LS, Pur. of Pub. Supplies, RG 92, NA; Irvine to Amasa Stetson, 5 Aug. 1813, LS, CG of P, RG 92, NA; Irvine to Acting Sec. of War, 29 July 1817, CG of P, LS, RG 92, NA. See also Knotel, *Handbuch der Uniformkunde . . .*, 3d ed. (Hamburg, 1937), and J. Margerand, "Les Coiffures de L'Armée Française," (Paris, 1909–1811), part III. Actually, the yeoman crown was in wide use by both the French and German infantry as early as 1807. The British infantry, however, adopted this cap only in 1816. See Cattley, "The British Infantry Shako," op. cit. Unfortunately, there is no specimen of the American Regular Army yeoman crown known to exist.

[61] *General Regulations for the Army* (Philadelphia, 1821), p. 155; Cattley "The British Infantry Shako," op. cit. European use of the "bell crown" style is shown in many contemporary prints.

[62] Adj. Gen. Daniel Parker to Irvine, 4 Apr. 1820, CCF (uniforms), RG 92, NA.

[63] *General Regulations for the Army* (1821), op. cit., p. 155. The term "yellow eagle" cited above is the "cap plate" listed in the Cost of Clothing lists included in the 1821 and 1825 regulations. The "small yellow button" mentioned as fitting in the leather cockade and described as having an eagle impressed on it is the "eagle" of the "cockades and eagles" in the same lists. In 1825 the pompons for light artillery companies were changed to yellow with red tops and those of the light infantry companies to white with red tops, adding red for grenadier companies "should the President order one per regiment to take this designation." See *General Regulations for the Army* (Washington, 1825). pp. 36, 157. Although the 1821 and 1825 regulations speak of "rifle companies," the Rifles as a separate branch of service had been disbanded in the reorganization of the Army in 1821. See Callan, op. cit., pp. 306–309.

[64] Irvine to Sec. of War, 7 Dec. 1821, CG of P, LS, RG 92, NA.

[65] Sec. of War to Irvine, 4 Jan. 1822, Sec. of War, LS, RG 107, NA.

[66] Dingee to Irvine, 20 Feb. 1830, CCF (Dingee), RG 92, NA.

[67] The sizes of the tops varied somewhat but in direct relation to the head size, as "7 inches head by 9⅛ inches bell . . . the whole to be 7 inches high." See contract with Henry Cressman, 24 Apr. 1822, CCF (Cressman), RG 92, NA.

[68] For this button, see David F. Johnson, *Uniform Buttons, American Armed Forces, 1784–1948*, 2 vols., (Watkins Glen, N.Y., 1948), vol. 1, p. 41.

[69] Campbell and Howell, op. cit., pp. 23–24.

[70] "Comparative Statement Showing Cost of Clothing," *American State Papers*, op. cit., vol. 2, p. 471. Oil cloth covers were supplied by Benjamin Morange and Son, painted linen covers by William Debaufre. See contracts with Morange dated 5 Jan. 1826 and 14 May 1827, in House Document 131, 19th Cong., 2d Sess., and Senate Document 72, 20th Cong., 1st Sess.; and contracts with Debaufre dated 11 Apr. 1830 and 25 Apr. 1831, in House Documents 73, 21st Cong., 2nd Sess. (serial 208), and 89, 22d Cong., 1st Sess. (serial 218); MSK "Journal" entries for 14 Sept. and 4 Oct. 1821, RG 92, NA.

[71] Irvine to Capt. S. W. Kearny, 10 Oct. 1821, CG of P, LS, RG 92, NA. There are numerous other instances of Irvine procuring officers' caps for them during this period.

[72] G.O. 53, Adjutant General's Office, 14 Aug. 1822, RG 94, NA.

[73] *General Regulations for the Army* (1821), op. cit., pp. 239–241; *General Regulations for the Army* (1825), op. cit., pp. 278–279.

IT IS EXTREMELY DIFFICULT TO DETERMINE just when the cap variously called "undress," "forage," or "fatigue" was first worn in the Army. Although there is no evidence that such a cap was a regulation item of wear prior to the turn of the 19th century, it is hard to believe that the more formal caps were the only type of headgear worn by the troops, especially on fatigue duty. European armies had been wearing some type of undress cap possibly as early as the middle of the 18th century, although references are somewhat vague and scattered. It is known that some British regiments as early as 1768 were wearing red forage caps lined with canvas, made of the remains of worn-out uniform coats, turned up in front with a small stiff flap of the facing cloth and with a falling cape in the rear.[74]

The first mention of such a cap in the American Regular Establishment is found in the Descriptive Book of the 1st Infantry dated 1801, under "Serjeants Dress and Men . . . the foraging Caps to be blue, Bound with red. . . ."[75] There seems to be no further official mention of such a cap until 1820. In the U.S. Marine Corps a "fatigue hat" of some sort was being worn in 1811 and a "leather fatigue cap" no later than 1818.[76] In 1817, however, Irvine directed the Military Storekeeper to issue, without charge to the soldier, the old felt caps which had been replaced with the leather models in 1813, "as a matter of accommodation to enable him to take better care of the leather cap."[77]

Although not mentioned in the 1821 uniform regulations, a "forage cap" priced at 39 cents, an item "not allowed" in 1817, appeared in the cost of clothing list in the general regulations for that year.[78] First approved in the spring of 1820, and admittedly "inferior in point of ornament" to the pattern approved for issue in 1825, it was described as being both "comfortable and convenient, comfortable in as much as it is light and may be worn so as to cover the greater part of the face and jaws, which is considered to be important in a cold climate, convenient because it can be rolled up so as to occupy but a small space in a knapsack without receiving injury."[79] These caps were not made on contract, but rather were cut out at the Clothing Establishment at Schuylkill Arsenal and assembled by seamstresses in the area on a piecework basis.[80] Nothing more is known of them except that they were of gray wool and that the allowance was one per five year enlistment.[81] They were probably similar to those of "gray cloth" prescribed for the cadets at the Military Academy in 1824.[82] In any case, considering the price, they could hardly have been elaborate. In May 1821, apparently after issue of the caps had started, the Commissary General of Purchases, who never seems to have liked them, suggested to the Secretary of War that leather caps of the old pattern, that is of the "Waterloo" pattern, be issued to regiments in the interior who might cut them down and adapt them for fatigue wear "making unnecessary the issue of cloth forage caps for sometime to come." The suggestion was approved.[83]

In the spring of 1825 a new forage cap was designed in the War Department and a pattern cap sent to Irvine for his use. The Corps, or branch of service, of the wearer was to be designated by the color of the trimmings. Officers were to wear the number of their regiment and enlisted men the letter of their company, of either white or yellow metal with holes in the metal so that the piece could be sewed to the headband. Officers and enlisted men's caps were to differ only in quality.[84] For reasons of durability the bodies of the caps were to be made of "Sergeant's cloth"; however, the other materials were to be "of the cheapest kind."[85] The 1825 uniform regulations describe the cap as follows:

Company officers, when on duty, absent from their companies, will be allowed in uniform to wear a *chakos* (or foraging cap) of blue cloth, trimmed with lace, corresponding with that on the coat, and of the precise pattern of that deposited in the office of the commissary-general of purchases. The enlisted men will also wear a *chakos* of the same pattern, in lieu of foraging caps, trimmed with worsted braid, like that on their coats.[86]

It would be interesting to know the reason for calling this cap a *chakos* in this strangely worded regulation, since it is so utterly foreign to the accepted "shako" pattern. The word itself is borrowed from the Magyar *csakó,* and traditionally designated a tall, formal, peaked military hat.[87]

Eight of these caps have been examined, all basically identical except that the tops of four are of two-piece construction and the others of four-piece (figs. 20–22). All are of dark blue wool. The tops measure $11\frac{1}{2}$ inches in diameter with twenty cords of twisted worsted binding radiating from a button in the center over the sides and terminating in a $2\frac{1}{4}$ inch headband. The headbands, which are backed with burlap and faced inside with cotton "sweats," are edged top and bottom with $\frac{1}{4}$ inch worsted braid. Three of the sweatbands are of twill weave, five of plain weave. The braid on five is in a herring-bone pattern, that on the others is plain ribbed. The visors, or "pokes", $2\frac{1}{4}$ inches wide at the front center and $10\frac{1}{2}$ inches from side to side, are of painted leather and are sewn directly to the headbands. Each cap has a metal grommet covered with plaited cotton, and none has either a chin strap or a flap in back to cover the neck. None carries a maker's label or an inspector's mark. The cloth portions of these caps, like the uniforms of the period, were cut out under the direction of government inspectors and parcelled out to local seamstresses for piecework assembly, thus no makers' name appears. The visors were furnished and attached on contract by leather goods makers.[88] The worsted braid on three is white for infantry, on the other five, yellow for artillery. The twisted worsted binding on all

Figure 20.—Forage Cap, 1825–1832.

Figure 21.—Forage Cap, 1825–1832.

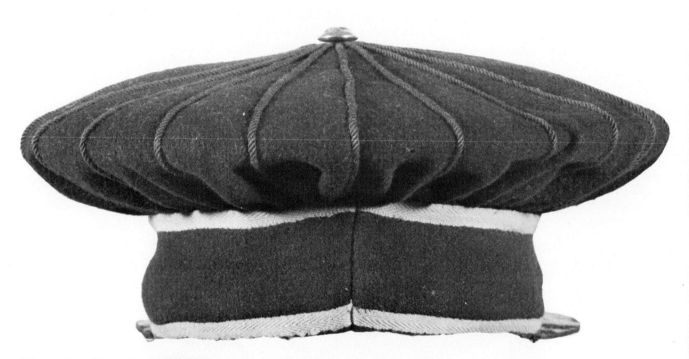

Figure 22.—Forage Cap, 1825–1832.

is dark green. Five of the buttons in the center of the tops are correct for the period and branch of service. There is no lining.

Compared with the leather dress caps of the period and preceding periods, the forage caps are rather crudely made. Clothing allowances called for the issue of but one during a five year enlistment, and no cap cover was issued with it [89]—although, oddly enough, a cover was issued with the leather cap—which led to numerous complaints from unit commanders because of its previousness to water and the fact that it was worn almost to the exclusion of the bell crown except when on guard or dress parade.[90] The cap was priced at $1.70 in 1826.[91]

NOTES

[74] Cecil C. P. Lawson, *A History of the Uniforms of the British Army* (London, 1961), vol. 3, pp. 44–46. Lawson's authority is Captain Cuthbertson, 5th Foot, in his *System for the Interior Management and Economy of an Infantry Battalion*, published in 1768 and again in 1776.

[75] Descriptive Book, 1st U.S. Infantry, Detroit, 1 Oct. 1801, U.S. Commands, RG 98, NA.

76 Lt. Col. Franklin Wharton, Commandant, to Capt. John Hall, 7 Jan. 1811; Maj. Rich. Smith to Maj. Archibald Henderson, 11 Oct. 1818—both quoted in E. N. McClellan, *Uniforms of the American Marines, 1775 to 1827* (Washington, 1932), pp. 48, 59.

77 Irvine to John Fellows, MSK, 8 Feb. 1817, CG of P, LS, RG 92, NA.

78 *General Regulations for the Army* (1821), op. cit., p. 239; "Comparative Statement of Clothing," *American State Papers*, op. cit., vol. 1, p. 471. This price rose to 50 cents in 1825; see, *General Regulations for the Army* (1825), op. cit., p. 277.

79 Irvine to Col. G. M. Brook, 4th Inf., 14 June 1820; Irvine to Sec. of War, 25 Apr. 1825—both CG of P, LS, RG 92, NA.

80 Undated, unsigned note in Box 1004, CCF (Schuylkill Arsenal), RG 92, NA.

81 Irvine to 1st Auditor, 31 Mar. 1820; Irvine to Sec. of War John C. Calhoun, 6 Nov. 1820, both in Irvine Account Book, MS Div., Library of Congress; Jesup to Capt. John Monroe, 4th Arty., 22 Oct. 1827, QMG, Cloth. Bk, LS, RG 92, NA.

82 Brig. Gen. Thomas Jesup, the Quartermaster General, to Capt. John Monroe, 4th Arty., 22 Oct. 1827, QMC, Cloth. Bk. LS, RG 92, NA; Frederick P. Todd, "The Leather Forage Cap at West Point," *Military Collector & Historian* (June 1954), vol. 6, no. 2, pp. 38–40.

83 Irvine to Sec. of War, 23 May 1821, CG of P, LS, RG 92, NA; Calhoun to Irvine, 31 May 1821, War Dept., Military Book 11, p. 216, RG 107, NA.

84 Inmes Barbour, War Dept., to Irvine, 16 April 1825, CCF (caps), RG 92; Jesup to Lt. H. Brown, Fort Columbus, N.Y., 31 Aug. 1829, Cloth. Bk., LS, RG 92; Irvine to Geo. Armitage, 7 June 1825, CG of P, LS, RG 92—all NA.

85 Irvine to Sec. of War, 25 Apr. 1825, CG of P, LS, RG 92, NA. "Sergeant's cloth" referred to the dark blue wool used in making sergeant's coats and of somewhat better quality than that used in privates' uniforms.

86 *General Regulations for the Army* (1825), op. cit., p. 157.

87 Walter Transfeldt and Karl-Hermann Frhr. v. Brand, *Wort und Brachtum des Soldaten . . .* (Hamburg, 1959), pp. 214–215. Cattley, op. cit., gives an excellent history of the origin of the word.

88 See contract with H. Cressman, 23 Apr. 1831, CCF (Cressman), RG 92, NA. For procedures in the procurement of clothing at this period, see Erna Risch, *Quartermaster Support of the Army, A History of the Corps* (Washington, 1962), pp. 144–152, 201–202.

89 *General Regulations for the Army* (1825), op. cit., p. 278.

90 Jesup to Maj. F. S. Belton, 2d Arty., 20 Jan. 1829; Jesup to Sec. of War John H. Eaton, 12 Nov. 1830—both in Cloth. Bk., LS, RG 92, NA.

91 *American State Papers*, op. cit., vol. 3, p. 352.

THE 1832 UNIFORM REGULATIONS prescribed a cap of "black beaver, 6 inches deep, with lacquered sunk tip, 11 inches in diameter, communicating by black leather side straps, with a band of the same, which is to encircle the bottom of the cap; black patent leather peak; gilt eagle, number, and scales as at present worn." [92] This was a return to the yeoman crown cap worn by the light and foot artillery and rifle regiments during the War of 1812 and a definite continuation of British influence.[93] Indeed, Major John Garland, head of the Clothing Bureau in August 1832 wrote General John E. Wool, the Inspector General of the Army then on an official trip abroad, to send home patterns of British uniforms and equipment for the use of the Clothing Bureau, stating "for I perceive we have copied from the English in most of the changes which have been made. . . ." [94] Despite this and the fact that Wool did forward a number of British uniforms,[95] the cap was not adopted and there is no evidence that it was ever made up in pattern form. Actually, the regulations were hardly off the press before Garland wrote Irvine that "some further change [was] contemplated in the uniform cap." [96] By March 1833 a new pattern cap had been made and approved and contracts let.[97] When it was first issued is not known, but it seems probable that it was available for recruits in mid-1833, as Cressman, one of the early contractors, was well known for his reliability in meeting delivery schedules. In any case, in July 1834 all leather caps of the 1821 pattern were ordered turned in, the surplus being sold to the Marine Corps which continued to use the bell crown for several years.[98]

General Regulations for the Army issued in 1834 describe the officers' cap as: [99]

> . . . black beaver, seven and a half inches deep, with lackered sunk tip seven and a half inches diameter,

with a band of black patent leather to encircle the bottom of the cap; black patent leather peak, gilt eagle and cross cannons [a "silver bugle" in the case of the infantry] and number of regiment as at present worn; [100] a strap of black patent leather, fastened to each side of the cap, to be worn under the chin. Plume—red cock-feathers [white for infantry], falling

Figure 23.—Infantry Cap, 1832–1851.

Figure 24.—Infantry Cap, 1832–1851.

from an upright stem, eight inches long, with a gilt socket.

.   .   .   .

The cap of the non-commissioned officers, musicians, and privates, to be of the same pattern as that designated for the officers. . . . Sergeant major— . . . plume, red upright hackle, [white for infantry] twelve inches long . . . Quartermaster sergeant—the same as the sergeant major excepting that the plume will be of light blue. Chief musician—the same as quartermaster sergeant . . . plume   white . . . Musicians— . . . white plume, upright hackle, ten inches long . . . . The plumes of the sergeants, corporals, and privates, red worsted [white for infantry] eight inches long.[101]

Two items omitted from the descriptive portions of the Regulations on the cap ornaments are the "tulip," which is actually a brass plume holder so-called because of its form, and, in the case of the enlisted men's cap, a metal number.[102] In 1839 officers of horse artillery were authorized red horsehair plumes instead of cock feathers.[103] In 1845 enlisted personnel of both light and horse artillery were authorized horsehair plumes and bands and tassels.[104]

Although Garland said much of the 1832 uniform was copied from the British, this cap, cylindrical in form, was a radical departure. It was more nearly French in origin and design and represented the first of an almost unbroken line of caps based on those of the French Army, patterns which continued until the adoption of the helmet for mounted units in 1872. This is not without explanation, for American officers were officially visiting France as well as Britain during this period. In addition to sending home British materials, General Wool forwarded to Washington from Paris in 1832 drawings of all current French uniforms.[105] The British Army and many elements of the French Army retained the yeoman crown cap for some years, but French light cavalry units had adopted a cylindrical pattern toward the end of the Napoleonic era. Although there is no specific mention of French influence on record, an examination of headgear of the period leads one to conclude that this modification was most probably based on the French cavalry pattern.[106]

Fourteen of these caps have been examined (figs. 23–25) and all follow the official description with tolerances of no more than ¼ to ½ inch. All are enlisted men's models of heavy felted wool rather than the black beaver prescribed for officers [107] and measure 7½ to 7¾ inches in height, with a top diameter of 7½ inches, and the jacked leather crown or "tip," sunken ½ inch and lapping over the sides 1 inch. The bottom of the cap carries a 1 inch leather band with a 3 inch soft leather sweatband welted to it on the outside, folded under, and fitted with a drawstring. The visor, or "poke," is convex and somewhat pointed, measuring 3 inches at its widest and 12 inches side to side, the underside painted green in some cases, black in others.[108] The sliding chin strap, with brass buckle and leather keeper, terminates in plain brass buttons wired to the cap at either end of the visor. In most cases the insignia is affixed to the cap with wooden pegs running through stapes. Although most of the caps carry the label "H. T. Gratacap 392 Broadway, N.Y.," others carry the labels of John Holloway, William Cressman, and Wm. H. Horstmann.[109] This cap was also worn by the "engineer soldiers" of the Company of Sappers, Miners, and Pontoniers when that unit was formed in

Figure 25.—Infantry Cap, 1832–1851.

1846 and was officially termed a "shako" for that unit. It had a black worsted, spherical pompon 3 inches in diameter instead of the tall plume, and a large engineer castle beneath the prescribed eagle as a cap plate.[110] The chin strap buttons on the specimen in the national collections are of the standard engineer pattern of the period.

One documented specimen of an officer's cap of this model is known. It conforms closely with the enlisted mens although of superior materials and workmanship (fig. 26). The most noticeable difference is in the visor, which is flat rather than convex and stitched at the edge, indicating two-piece construction.[111]

There were many pros and cons as to the practicability of this cap, with the cons predominating. Whereas several of the more clothes-conscious officers such as Philip Kearney liked the cap and thought it compared favorably with European dress headgear,[112] there were numerous complaints regarding it from the frontier posts. Colonel George Croghan, the Inspector General

28

Figure 26.—Artillery Officer's Cap, 1832–1851.   West Point Museum.

in the West, reported that it was "much complained of . . . and with reason" and as a result was seldom worn except for guard duty or on dress parade.[113]

Initial manufacturing difficulties apparently account for the first contract for this cap being let at the rather high price of $2.37½ for the cap alone.[114] By 1835 the price had dropped to $1.74 and by 1840 to $1.58.[115] This price did not include the insignia and pompon holders, or "tulips." Pompons were supplied by other contractors and increased the price by more than 50 cents.[116] Two caps were allowed for each five-year enlistment.[117]

NOTES

[92] Order No. 50. H.Q. of the Army, 11 June 1832, RG 94, NA.

[93] The British continued the yeoman crown cap until 1844. See Cattley, "The British Infantry Shako," op. cit.

[94] Garland to Wool, 10 Aug. 1832, Cloth. Bur., LS, RG 92, NA.

[95] Three cases of British material were received in Jan. 1833. See D. Stimson, QM representative in New York, to

Garland, 15 Jan. 1833, Cloth. Bur., LR, tray 61, RG 92, NA.

[96] Garland to Irvine, 11 July 1832, Cloth. Bur., LS, RG 92, NA. This "uniform cap" referred to the dress cap, not the forage cap, for the latter was mentioned separately several lines below in the same letter. See also Lt. A. B. Eaton, 2d Inf., to Cloth. Bur., 8 Aug. 1833, Cloth. Bur., LR, tray 61, RG 92, NA.

[97] Contract with Henry Cressman, Philadelphia, 26 Mar. 1833, CCF (Cressman), RG 92, NA.

[98] G.O. 53, H.Q. of the Army, 26 July 1834, RG 94, NA; Garland to Irvine, 21 Oct. 1833, Cloth. Bur., LS, RG 92, NA; Irvine to Fayssoux, 16 June 1834, CG of P, LS, RG 92, NA.

[99] Until the 1832 regulations only company grade officers of the line corps were required to wear the cap, while those above the rank of captain wore the chapeau. Now field grade officers of the line were to wear the cap while on duty with troops but were granted the privilege of wearing a cocked hat on other occasions. This change upset some senior officers. See Garland to Col. D. Baker, 6th Inf., 20 Mar. 1833, Cloth. Bur. LS, RG 92, NA.

[100] On this insignia see Campbell and Howell, op. cit., pp. 26–27.

[101] General Regulations for the Army (Washington, 1834), pp. 218–230.

[102] Ibid., p. 210. These appear in the cost of clothing list.

[103] G.O. 36, H.Q. of the Army, 21 June 1839, RG 94, NA.

[104] G.O. 54, H.Q. of the Army, 15 Dec. 1845. The cap on which these were worn may have been a modification of the dragoon cap as recommended by the 1844 Uniform Board. In any case, the price was higher than that of the foot artillery cap.

[105] Detmar H. Finke and Frederick P. Todd, "French Influence on Early Uniforms of the United-States Army," Revue Historique de l'Armee (special issue, 1957), p. 58.

[106] H. Malibran, Guide a l'usage des artistes et des costumiers . . . (Paris, 1904); J. Margerand, "Les coiffures de l'armee francaise," op. cit.; Knotel, op. cit., p. 177.

[107] Irvine described this material as "coney fur or wool" imported from South America. See Irvine to Wm. Silkman, Whitlocksville, N.Y., 26 Dec. 1836, CG of P, LS, RG 92, NA.

[108] Although the officers' visors were prescribed as "patent" leather, those on the enlisted model were of "stout well prepared leather." See ibid.

[109] See Appendix.

[110] G.O. 18, H.Q. of the Army, 4 June 1846, RG 94, NA. On the insignia see Campbell and Howell, op cit., pp. 27–28.

[111] Cap worn by Lt. David E. Hale, 1st Arty., USMA class of 1833 in West Point Museum collections.

[112] See J. Watts De Peyster, Personal and Military History of Philip Kearny (New York, 1869), pp. 57–58. Kearny attended the French Cavalry School at Saumur in 1839–1840.

[113] Francis Paul Prucha, ed., Army Life on the Western Frontier . . . (Norman, Okla., 1958), p. 62; Jesup to Sec. of War, 12 Nov. 1830, Cloth. Bk., LS, RG 92, NA.

[114] On these difficulties see Garland to Irvine, 10 Dec. 1832, Cloth. Bur., LS; A. Russell Jr. and Co. to Garland, 28 Feb. 1833, Cloth. Bur., LR—both in RG 92, NA.

[115] Contract with Cressman, 7 Jan. 1835, CCF (Cressman), RG 92, NA; cost of clothing list in G.O. 42, H.Q. of the Army, 6 Oct. 1840, RG 94, NA.

[116] Ibid. One of the early suppliers of metal insignia for this cap was Anson Baker of New York, while W. H. Horstmann of Philadelphia supplied pompons. William Pinchin of Philadelphia also supplied metal insignia. See contract with Anson Baker, 16 Jan. 1835, in CCF (caps), RG 92, NA. There are numerous references to Pinchin and Horstmann in CG of P letter books for this period. See also "Statement of Cost of Clothing for the Army, 1834," in General Regulations for the Army (Washington, 1835), p. 210.

[117] G.O. 67, H.Q. of the Army, 31 July 1832; G.O. 56, H.Q. of the Army, 4 Dec. 1838—both RG 94, NA.

☆DRAGOON CAP, 1833–1851☆

ORDER NO. 38, HEADQUARTERS OF THE ARMY, 2 May 1833, which described the uniform of the newly authorized United States Regiment of Dragoons, prescribed the officer's cap as follows: ". . . of the same material as that for the Infantry, but according to a pattern furnished; to be ornamented with a gilt star, silver eagle, and gold cord; the star to be worn in front, with a drooping white horsehair pompon; the Field Officers to have a *small* strip of red hair, to show in front of their pompons." For the enlisted men the same order states: "Cap—Same material as for other Corps, but the pattern, ornaments and trimmings, like the one furnished the Clothing Bureau. Drooping white horsehair pompon." [118] The only known detailed description of this cap is in a letter from Callender Irvine to a prospective supplier:

> The tops of the uniform caps are of pretty stout jacked leather made to fit . . . precisely. They extend down the bodies of the caps one inch and are neatly stitched to the lower edge. . . . The Dragoon cap is level on top, the poke . . . is *patent* leather. The bodies . . . are made of imported materials, so said, from South America and coney fur or wool is the principal thereof. There is a strap of *patent* leather with a slide . . ., so fixed as to be brought under the chin to secure the cap to the head. . . . [119]

An element of the cap trimming not prescribed in the original order is the "brass grenade" mentioned in the cost of clothing list of the same year. [120] A variation of the well-known "flaming bomb" device with a plume holder attached behind, it is the equivalent of the infantry and artillery "tulip," although somewhat smaller. Similarly, although the original order did mention a gold "cord" for officers it omitted the "band" for the enlisted men. [121] Following the general usage in the Army at the time, it is probable that the officers' "cord" was of gold colored metallic cord. The enlisted

version was of yellow worsted. [122] No description of this "cord," "band," or "band and tassel," as it was variously termed, has been found. The only contemporary illustrations giving any appreciable detail show this cord fastened on either side of the top of the crown, falling in plaited form in front and behind and extending down the left side as two single cords with a tassel near the top, continuing down the back, coming under the right arm, and terminating in two rather elaborate knots and tassels attached to the breast of the wearer. [123] In this form, it added much color to the uniform and served to attach the cap in the same manner as a pistol lanyard.

A number of identical specimens of this cap have survived (figs. 27–29). Generally similar to the 1832 infantry and artillery pattern, of the same heavy felted woolen material, and indicating the same French influence, there is nonetheless a definite visible difference. While the infantry-artillery cap is cylindrical, the dragoon cap is taller and somewhat conical, being 8¼ inches high and measuring but 6½ inches across the crown, which is flat rather than "sunken" and 7 or more inches across the base depending on size. The visor, rather than pointed and convex, is flat, 3¼ inches wide at the center and 11½ inches from side to side, and the chin strap terminates in regulation dragoon rather than plain buttons. In other respects the caps are similar. They were made by, among others, Cressman, Gratacap, and Ernest C. Smith of Philadelphia. [124] The gold or yellow "bands and tassels" with the specimens described are very similar to the "cords and bands" worn on the helmets from 1872 to 1902 and minutely described in specifications published by the Quartermaster General in 1887. [125] It is possible that these bands and tassels are not original but the 1872 pattern added to these caps at a later date. The price for the enlisted men's model was 70 cents. [126]

Figure 27.—Dragoon Cap, 1833–1851.

Figure 28.—Dragoon Cap, 1833–1851.

In 1832, when the infantry-artillery cap was yet in the developmental stages, Irvine had expressed considerable doubt as to the advisability of using wool felt as opposed to leather for the body of the cap.[127] As the result of three years experience with the felted models, he had Henry Cressman make up a model in 1836 in light, durable leather which he sent to the Clothing Bureau for submission to the Secretary of War with a commentary that was both an example of his practicality as Commissary General of Purchases and of the growing nationalism of the times. It also echoes his feelings on the subject expressed in 1813. He wrote Garland:

I have forwarded to your address a leathern cap, which, on its receipt, I will thank you to submit to the examination of the Secretary of War. I propose its adoption in lieu of the cap now in use with the Army for

the following reasons. It is made entirely of a material the production of our country, to be had in abundance, and which is known to be durable. It is lighter by two or three ounces than the present cap, a matter of some moment. . . . Such caps can be completed in one shop, or by one mechanic, and can be supplied in any required numbers in a short time. The competition in supplying such caps will be great, whereas the principal material in the present cap is of foreign growth, is imported in small quantities, gets into the hands of speculators by which competition is lessened and there is but one person, known to me, who understands the composition and manufacture of the materials.[128]

The suggested change was never made.

There was much dissatisfaction with both the infantry-artillery and dragoon models expressed by troops in the field. Although established to deal primarily with the quantity of caps issued the troops, the 1844 Uniform Board recommended several changes:

UNIFORM CAP

For Dragoons—To be lower behind, giving a surface to rest on the head instead of an edge—and to rise gradually to the front—the visor to be reduced in width, and to be cut according to the pattern furnished—For mounted Artillery—according to the modified pattern, the band and tassel red, the plume of red horse-hair—For Ordnance, Artillery, and Infantry according to the pattern exhibited by Col. Stanton—The same improvement as for Drags . . . . The principal advantages to be derived from the foregoing modifications are these—The uniform cap for Dragoons which as now constructed is liable in rapid movement to be thrown off and exceedingly painful to the head, will retain its place, and be supported with more ease to the wearer. . . .[129]

These modifications were probably never made prior to the 1851 uniform change. Certainly no specimens are known which conform. The band and tassel and the red horsehair plume, however, were adopted for the mounted artillery.[130]

NOTES

[118] In RG 94, NA. In regard to the "gilt star, silver eagle," Campbell and Howell, op. cit., p. 26, states that "the eagle is basically the Napoleonic type adopted by the British after the Battle of Waterloo and altered by omitting the lightning bolts in the talons and adding a wreath to the breast." This is not correct. M. Jean Brunon of Marseilles, the distinguished French military historian and collector of French militaria, has informed the authors: "Among the 13 Eagles taken by the English (11 in Spain, 2 at Waterloo) only the Eagle of the 8th Regiment of the French Line lost by us at the battle of

Figure 29.—Dragoon Cap, 1833–1851.

Chiclana [called the Battle of Barrosa by the British] March 5, 1811, carried the golden wreath given by the City of Paris upon the return of the Grand Army after the campaigns of Austerlitz, Jena, and Friedland, 1805 to 1807. This wreath in solid gold encircles the neck of the Eagle and is tied to it . . . ." M. Jean Brunon to Melvin H. Jackson, 10 Jan. 1965, LR in S.I. files. The eagle captured at Chiclana was taken by the 87th Foot (Royal Irish Fusiliers) and at various periods that unit has used it on its badges and buttons; see H. G. Parkyn, *Shoulder-Belt Plates and Buttons* (Aldershot, 1956), pp. 302–05.

[119] Irvine to Wm. Silkman, Whitlockville, N.Y., 26 Dec. 1836, CG of P, LS, RG 92, NA.

[120] *General Regulations for the Army* (1834), op. cit., p. 210.

[121] Ibid.

[122] House Document No. 2, 26th Cong., 1st Sess., p. 271.

[123] "U.S. Dragoon Corps, Full Dress," *U.S. Military Magazine* (Feb. 1841), no plate number; sketch by Frank B. Mayer, "United States Cavalry, First Dragoons, 1851," White MSS, New York Public Library.

[124] Three of the specimens studied carry the labels of these makers. See appendix for contract dates.

[125] Specification No. 188, QMG's Office, 5 Apr. 1887, RG 92, NA.

[126] Cost of clothing list for 1840 in G.O. 46, H.Q. of the Army, 6 Oct. 1840, RG 94, NA.

[127] Irvine to Garland, 30 Oct. 1832, tray 61, Cloth. Bur., LR, RG 92, NA.

[128] Irvine to Garland, 12 May 1836, CG of P, LS, RG 92, NA.

[129] Uniform Board Report, 27 Apr. 1844, A.G. Doc. File B 136, 1844, Box 150, RG 94, NA. This report is very difficult to use because marginal notations (apparently made by the Quartermaster General as it was routed to him by the Adjutant General) indicating whether certain recommendations were approved or not, are all but illegible.

[130] These items appear for the first time in a cost of clothing list in G.O. 54, H.Q. of the Army, 15 Dec. 1845, RG 94, NA.

I T IS UNCERTAIN whether the retention of the 1825 forage cap pattern was intended at the time the 1832 uniform regulations were written, or whether a new pattern was to be selected. The regulations state merely "according to pattern." In any case, in July 1832 Major Garland, head of the Clothing Bureau in Washington, wrote Irvine that a forage cap was to be selected in a few days and a sample forwarded to Philadelphia.[131] This cap is first officially mentioned in Order No. 38, Headquarters of the Army, 2 May 1833, which describes the uniform for the newly organized United States Regiment of Dragoons, prescribing a forage cap of "Black leather, like pattern furnished clothing Bureau" (figs. 30–32). A distinct change from the 1825 cap, the pattern was adopted for the entire

Army and the Corps of Cadets at the Military Academy as well. Although the troops were to continue to wear the older cap until stocks were exhausted,[132] the 7th Infantry at least was issued the new model as early as the late spring of 1833.[133] The change in price from $1.30 to 87½ and 75 cents for dragoon and "other" caps respectively in the 1833 clothing price list also indicates the cutoff date. The cadets donned the new cap in 1834.[134]

No reasons are known for this rather radical change in style of the forage cap—adopted in pattern form in mid-1832 for both the officers and enlisted men of the infantry and artillery—except for repeated complaints regarding the practicability of the old pattern.[135] There is no known foreign influence in this instance. Contem-

Figure 30.—Forage Cap, 1833–1839.

Figure 31.—Forage Cap, 1833–1839.

Figure 32.—Forage Cap, 1833–1839.

porary descriptions are scanty, Major Garland merely stating that it was "of leather with a patent leather visor . . . made with one fold at the top; the only ornament . . . the letter of the Company placed in front." "The letter . . . is to be yellow in all cases."[136] The dragoon caps differed from those for the infantry and artillery in having wider visors and folds in the back which could be let down some 6 inches to cover the neck in bad weather.[137] For winter wear in cold climates a band of black fur 2½ inches wide, attached to the bottom and tied in front, was prescribed.[138] The caps for the line units were to be of morocco, those for the cadets at the Military Academy of goatskin.[139] The precise measurements of the cap were given as follows:

Poke from point to point 7¾ inches
Poke width in center 3 inches
Depth of crown, center 7½ inches
Breadth across top center 7½ inches
Length of top 12½ inches
Depth of hood 6½ inches

Length of hood connected with crown 14½ inches
Length of hood at bottom 16½ inches [140]

Priced at 87½ cents for dragoons and 75 for the other branches in 1833 and 1834, the price leveled at 80 cents for all branches in 1835 and 1836, but rose to 85 for dragoons and dropped to 75 for other branches in 1837 and 1838.[141] The price to the Corps of Cadets was much higher—$2.00, which included the profit allowed the storekeeper.[142] This would indicate that the line units received imitation and the cadets genuine morocco.

There are several contemporary illustrations of the cap: one in an engraving after a painting by Robert W. Weir, another in an engraving by R. Wallis after W. H. Bartlett, several, although rather poor as to detail, in paintings by George Catlin, and an excellent one (fig. 33) by Seth Eastman done in Florida in 1840–1841. Two Edwin Forbes drawings in Rodenbough's *From Everglade to Canyon with the Second Dragoons* . . . . show the dragoon form of the cap, but they were

Figure 33.—Infantryman wearing 1833–1839 Forage Cap. Watercolor by Seth Eastman. Knoedler Galleries.

executed many years after it had become obsolete. Their accuracy, however, indicates that the artist may well have had an actual specimen from which to work.[143]

The only cap examined is that which came to the Museum with the old War Department Collection. It is of well-finished black leather and measures 20 inches from side to side when folded, with a plain black patent leather visor 3 inches at widest and 8¾ inches side to side. The cap proper is of three-piece construction, back, top, and front, with a triangular piece set into the front, and constructed so that it can be folded, the crease running from ear to ear. The whole is pieced together with round leather welting at the seams and at the base of the visor. A sweatband, 1¼ inches on the inside and of the same material as the cap, has been sewn to the outside and turned under. A ½ inch sliding chin strap terminates at either end of the visor in regulation buttons. From the terminals of the chin strap a 1¼ inch band runs around the back of the cap. There is no evidence of a hood ever having been attached, which indicates that it was an infantry or artillery model. There is no lining and no maker's name or inspector's initials.

Although the cap was somewhat ungainly looking—indeed, the cadets had to be warned as to the proper way it should be worn [144]—it seemed practical and durable and was certainly an improvement over the earlier patterns. The Superintendent of the Military Academy noted in 1839 that the cap "though a most unbecoming one, has great merit on the score of economy and durability." [145] The line units, however, filed numerous complaints as to its durability, especially in relation to the allowance of one in every five years, and asked that the allowance be increased.[146] The caps were also sold by the Commissary General of Purchases to post sutlers for resale to the troops, further evidence they were not lasting the prescribed five years.[147]

NOTES

[131] Garland to Irvine, 11 July 1832, Cloth. Bur., LS, RG 92, NA. This pattern cap was forwarded on 10 Aug. See Garland to Irvine, 10 Aug. 1832, Cloth. Bur., LS, RG 92, NA.

[132] G.O. 53, H.Q. of the Army, 26 July 1834, RG 94, NA.

[133] Irvine to Fayssoux, 10 Apr. 1833, CG of P, LS, RG 92, NA.

[134] "Comparative Statement of Cost of Clothing," *American State Papers*, op. cit., vol. 4, p. 764, vol. 5, p. 448; Order No. 87, USMA, 23 July 1833, quoted in Todd, "The Leather Forage Cap at West Point," op. cit.

[135] Garland to Irvine, 11 July and 10 Aug. 1832, Cloth. Bur., LS, RG 92, NA.

[136] Garland to Capt. Charles Thurston, 23 Apr. 1833; Garland to Irvine, 10 Aug. 1832—both in Cloth. Bur., LS, RG 92, NA.

[137] Irvine to Wm. Morange, 3 May 1833, CG of P, LS, RG 92, NA. See also Maj. D. Winder (?), 2d Drag., to Maj. Levi Whiting (then head of the Cloth. Bur.), 16 Dec. 1840, Cloth. Bur., LR, RG 92, NA.

[138] *General Regulations for the Army* (Washington, 1834), op. cit., p. 228.

[139] Contract with Wm. Hill, 31 Jan. 1838, Cloth. Bur., LR, tray 57, RG 92, NA. This contract called for dragoon forage caps of Curacao Morocco at 75 cents. For the cadet caps see Order No. 87, USMA, 23 July 1833, quoted in Todd, "The Leather Forage Cap at West Point," op. cit. Morocco leather is generally defined as goatskin tanned with sumac, or any imitation thereof. See Peter C. Welsh, *Tanning in the United States to 1850, A Brief History,* U.S. National Museum Bulletin 242 (Washington, 1964), pp. 88–90.

[140] Irvine to Morange, 3 May 1833, CG of P, LS, RG 92, NA.

[141] "Comparative Statement of Cost of Clothing," *American State Papers*, op. cit., vol. 5, p. 447, vol. 7, p. 628.

[142] Todd, "The Leather Forage Cap at West Point," op. cit.

[143] See T. F. Rodenbough, *From Everglade to Canyon with the Second Dragoons . . .* (New York, 1875), p. 17; Forbes was born in 1839 and began to study art in 1857. See also *The Civil War, A Centennial Exhibition of Eyewitness Drawings* (Washington, 1961), p. 116.

[144] Todd, "The Leather Forage Cap at West Point," op. cit.

[145] Maj. Richard Delafield to Col. J. G. Totten, 20 Sept. 1839, quoted in ibid.

[146] Garland to Irvine, 15 Apr. 1835, Cloth. Bur., LS, RG 92, NA. In 1833, when the pattern caps were being examined, Irvine stated that he thought they should be made of a more durable leather such as cordovan; see Irvine to Garland, 5 Feb. 1833, Cloth. Bur., LR, tray 61, RG 92, NA. Obviously the line troops put their caps to much harder usage than the cadets.

[147] Brown and Earleth, sutlers at Sackets Harbor, to Irvine, 12 Oct. 1838, CCF (caps), RG 92, NA.

Sometime during the winter of 1838–1839 Major General Alexander Macomb, Commanding the Army, determined on a change in the leather forage cap which had been regulation since 1832. Macomb had always shown an unusual interest in all items of the Army's dress, but no reasons for this particular change have come to light. His decision was probably influenced, however, by the rather unattractive appearance of the leather cap, no matter what its practicality, plus the popularity of the flat, cloth visored cap, similar to the 1825–1833 pattern, in both the British Army as an undress hat and American racing and hunting circles as an informal sporting or "hacking" cap.[148]

Following a tour of inspection of a number of installations in the northeast, Macomb went to Florida in the late winter of 1839 where a good portion of the Army was struggling with the knotty problem of the removal of the Seminoles. Sometime before his departure for Florida he had proposed a cap change to the Secretary of War and been told to go ahead. On 17 April he wrote Major Levi Whiting, then head of the Clothing Bureau, inclosing drawings and a brief description of a new cap he had in mind. The officers' model was to be of dark blue cloth with a chin strap of black patent leather and a silk oil cloth cover for bad weather. Enlisted personnel were to be issued a cap of similar design and cloth, but without ornament except for colored cap bands, red for artillery, white for infantry, yellow for dragoons, and sky blue for ordnance. Officers' ornaments were to be embroidered on separate pieces of cloth which might be put on or taken off at pleasure. He instructed Whiting to contact Mr. St. John in New York and have him make pattern caps for officers.[149]

Whiting replied that Macomb's drawings had been copied at the Topographical Bureau, approved by the Secretary of War, and were then being lithographed. The Secretary had decided that the caps of the officers

and men were to be alike, that "bands"—presumably the colored bands—were to be added to the officers' caps, and that the ornaments were to be of metal rather than embroidery.[150] The lithographs (fig. 34), which were in color, were forwarded to St. John with the request that pattern caps be furnished the Commissary General of Purchases so that he might have patterns made of the enlisted men's model to aid him in making his estimates for the next clothing year.[151]

The previous July the former Bureau of Topographical Engineers had been made an independent corps of the Army, and during the fall and winter a distinctive uniform for it had been under consideration by the War Department. In April 1839, Colonel John Abert, Chief of the Corps, submitted to the Secretary of War a description of the uniform complete with carefully delineated drawings of its components and trimmings, one of which (fig. 35) illustrated a forage cap almost identical to that in the lithograph prepared for Macomb.[152] Since both were prepared for lithographing at the Bureau, the two caps must be considered the same except for the cap band. In May the uniform regulation for the new Corps was approved and published. It described a forage cap as follows:

> Of dark blue cloth, with an oil silk cover, to be worn in rainy weather; black patent leather visor; cap band of black silk and worsted lace, two and one-fourth inches wide, with oak leaves and acorn figure. Device in front: a shield between two oak leaves, wrought of the same material and corresponding in form with the device at the bottom of the skirt of the coat. The whole to correspond with the pattern to be deposited in the Topographical Bureau. The forage cap must always be worn with the frock coat . . . .[153]

Although the cloth forage cap was approved in principle before summer and patterns of the officers' model had been made and forwarded to uniform makers, it was not until December that the final details

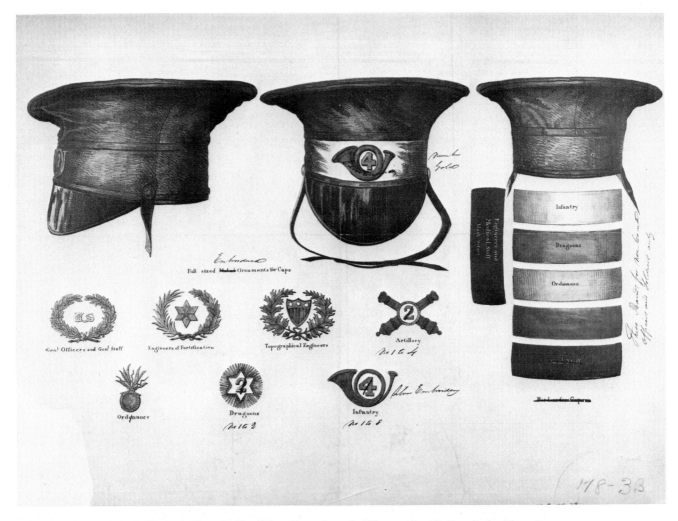

Figure 34.—Proposed Forage Cap, 1839. War Department lithograph. National Archives.

of the enlisted men's model were settled. The caps were to be made of a waterproof cloth developed by Samuel Lawrence of Lowell, Massachusetts, with a "cape" attached to the rear which could be lowered to cover the neck in bad weather. There were also several small changes in the chin strap.[154] Contracts were let early in 1840 at an average price of $1.30, although no caps were to be issued during the clothing year ending 31 October 1840.[155] The pattern was also adopted for the Corps of Cadets at West Point and the cap's price set at $2.34.[156]

Irvine experienced considerable difficulty with the contractors of these caps—he had had none with the dress cap makers—and in May 1841 he decided to have them made, as the clothing for the Army was, by outside seamstresses on a piecework basis, the leather trimmings to be bought on contract and added at the arsenal.[157] The "waterproofed" cloth furnished by

Lawrence also caused difficulties, and Irvine dropped him as a supplier and went to other sources for "waterproofed" fabric.[158]

Colored bands for forage caps were called for in the Macomb lithographs for both officers and enlisted men. The two extant copies of the print, however, carry the handwritten comment "These bands for non-comd. officers and soldiers only," and one the comment "No Bands for Officers." A letter from Major Whiting to a Mr. B. de la Pierce of New York states: "You will perceive by the written remarks that the colored bands have been dispensed with. . . ."[159] De la Pierce was a well-known hatter and uniform maker who apparently specialized in work for officers. There is no record of his having contracted to make caps for enlisted men. It must be inferred that Whiting meant bands were dispensed with for officers' caps only. No photograph of an officer wearing this headpiece with such a band

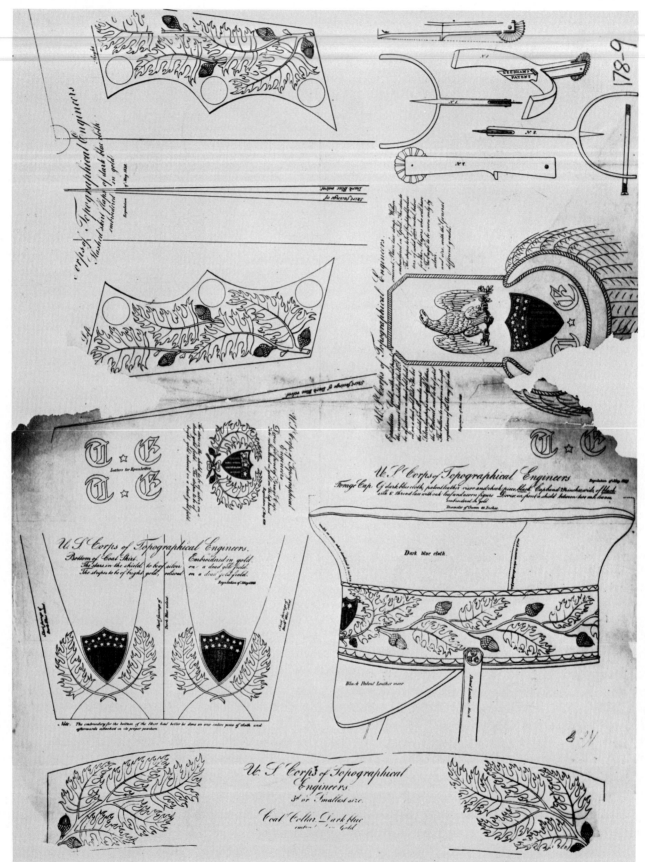

Figure 35.—Forage Cap for Topographical Engineers, 1839. War Department proof sheet. National Archives.

is known. On the other hand, a number of contemporary Mexican War illustrations show enlisted men wearing bands of white, red, and yellow. A careful search of Quartermaster General records for the period reveals no purchase of any material for such specific use.[160]

Illustrative of the care with which clothing estimates were made at this period is the following list of components and estimated costs of the forage cap in 1843–1844:[161]

Forage Cap—

7	inches 6/4 waterproof blue cloth	$ .53$17\frac{17}{36}$
9½	inches 7/8 muslin, unbleached	$1\frac{7}{12}$
2	skeins blue thread no. 35	$1\frac{1}{2}$
$\frac{1}{10}$	sheet of wadding	$1\frac{1}{24}$
2	buttons	$15\frac{3}{72}$
$\frac{3}{4}$	yards black galoon	$1\frac{5}{12}$
1	yard cane	$2\frac{1}{96}$
$\frac{3}{10}$	oz. curled hair	$7\frac{3}{160}$
	Leather trimmings	22½
	Cuttings & making	18
	Actual cost	$1.01$7\frac{7}{15}$
	Est. cost	1.01½

Another aspect must be considered. A number of these caps have been examined, all from the War Department Collection and thus assumed to be enlisted issue items. Some definitely show signs of wear, but none shows any evidence of ever having had a band attached, and all have the folded "cape" which could be let down to cover the neck in bad weather. Because of the cape and the positioning of the buttons at either end of the chin strap, the band would have had to go under the cape, thus largely negating its effectiveness as a distinguishing device. Oddly enough, the one known authenticated officer's cap (fig. 36)[162] and all the caps shown in contemporary photographs of officers are capeless (see also fig. 37). However, all the enlisted men's caps examined have capes, including one definite pattern piece. The best explanation for the appearance of the bands in so many contemporary illustrations is that they were secured by individual troop units and worn without War Department authorization. A known instance is the Regimental Band of the 1st Dragoons, which was authorized by the regimental commander "a double stripe (like Sergeants) on their

Figure 36.—Officer's Forage Cap, 1839–1851. West Point Museum.

Figure 37.—Lt. B. W. Armstrong, 1st Dragoons, ca. 1845.   National Archives.

Wool Overalls and two yellow bands of worsted or cloth around the Cap with the number of the Regiment on a blue ground in front." [163] It should be noted that while an organizational band wore the uniform of the regiment or corps to which it belonged, the commanding officer might purchase from post or company funds "such additions in ornaments as he may judge proper." [164]

The cadets at the Military Academy undoubtedly wore a band on their forage caps even though the regulars apparently did not. Since changes in cadet dress were generally settled—at least during this period—by direct correspondence between the Superintendent and the Secretary of War without reference to the Commanding General or the Quartermaster General,[165] this is not unusual. One such band has survived (fig. 38), worn by General George M. McClellan when a cadet 1842–1846. It is of black velvet, 2 inches wide and the edges turned under and tacked, 22½ inches in circumference.[166] The device "U S M A" in modified Old English script lies within a wreath of laurel with palm fronds on either side, the band of gold embroidery of highest quality and workmanship.

Probably as a concession to the bitter winter weather at West Point, the cadets were originally allowed to add a band of fur to the caps, a practice discontinued by order in 1843.[167] As in the case of the leather forage cap, the cadets had to be told how to wear the new one, a number of them having removed the stiffening of the crown to give a more rakish appearance.[168] It should be noted that no extant photograph of a cadet wearing this cap shows the presence of a cape as on the enlisted models. The order published in 1846 describing the dress of the newly organized Company of Sappers, Miners and Pontoniers, the "Engineer Soldiers", prescribed for wear on the forage cap a "band of black cotton velvet with a yellow castle in front according to drawing and pattern in clothing bureau".[169]

When the 1844 Uniform Board met it considered carefully both the quality of the forage cap and the quantity issued. It was the considered opinion of the members that (as had proved true with the 1825 pattern) one cap issued every five years was not sufficient. They recommended that one cap "as improved by Col. Stanton" be issued annually unless an oil cloth cover was provided (a commentary on the "water-proofed" cloth used). With the oil cloth cover, provided, caps should be issued three times in the five year period.[170] It is not known what Stanton's improvements were, but they apparently involved both the quality and the pattern.[171] Despite the recommendation of the board the cap continued to be issued only once in five years.

The caps that have been examined, supplemented by the officer's specimen (fig. 36)[172] fall into three basic types within the general pattern. Type one (figs. 39–41), which in profile is most similar to those illustrated in the lithographs, has a sharply pointed, almost perpendicular patent leather visor, 2½ inches at its widest and 10½ inches from side to side, welted to the headband with leather. A patent leather sliding chin strap immediately above the visor terminates in two brass general service buttons. The whole of the cap proper is of dark blue wool cloth. The crown is 10½ inches in diameter, with the rise to the crown of four pieces 2 inches high, welted to the crown. The headband is 2½ inches wide of one-piece construction. Attached to it is the "cape," 4 inches wide when unfolded, buttoned to the headband at the chin strap

Figure 38.—U.S. Military Academy Forage Cap Band, ca. 1842–1846.

Figure 39.—Forage Cap, 1839–1851, Type 1.

terminals, and tied across the front with black silk ribbons when folded. The whole of the interior of the cap is lined with unbleached muslin or with glazed cotton, with cotton batting between the lining and the crown and the rise. The headband is lined in front with pasteboard to give a firm seat for the insignia. The sweatband is of soft black patent leather. All but one specimen has a cane grommet in the welt between the crown and the rise. One specimen carries the remains of a round red wax seal on the sweatband indicating that it was probably a pattern piece.

Type two (figs. 42–46) is basically the same in appearance as type one except that the visor, rather than pointed and nearly perpendicular, is more nearly horizontal and rounded. The blue cloth is of a somewhat heavier quality, the crown is not padded, the padding between the lining and the rise is of horsehair, and the headband is reinforced all around with leather rather than pasteboard. Whether these changes constitute Colonel Stanton's improvements is not known.

Figure 40.—Forage Cap, 1839–1851, Type 1.

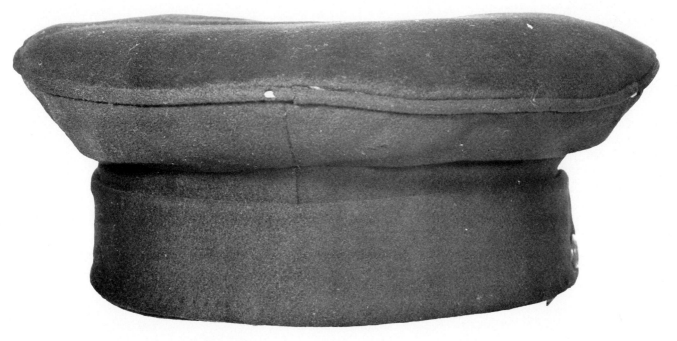

Figure 41.—Forage Cap, 1839–1851, Type 1.

Figure 42.—Forage Cap, 1839–1851, Type 2.

Figure 43.—Forage Cap, 1839–1851, Type 2.

Figure 44.—Forage Cap, 1839–1851, Type 2.

Figure 45.—Forage Cap, 1839–1851, Type 2.

Type three is identical to type two except that it carries no chin strap, and the cape, when folded, since it could not be buttoned to the chin strap buttons, is attached by means of a metal hook fitting into a threaded eye (fig. 47). This type is the latest of the three, dating no earlier than 1851, the cloth portions being machine-stitched throughout.[173] None of the specimens bears a maker's mark and, with the exception of the pattern piece, must be assumed to postdate Irvine's decision to manufacture the caps at Schuylkill.

The caps worn by officers in the several extant photographs and the Duncan cap in the West Point Museum are all type one. The only difference between this cap and that of the enlisted men is in the stitched visor.

The "water-proofed" feature of the cloth is interesting. If it was developed by Lawrence, who first submitted samples to the War Department, he did not patent it. The waterproofing was a method of treating

the cloth with a compound (ingredients unknown) rather than a method of weaving, for Lawrence also "water-proofed" cotton drilling and paper, the latter proposed for use in making cartridges.[174] In any case, the process was not successful as evidenced by the numerous complaints to the 1844 Uniform Board and the board's recommendations that an oil cloth cover be provided.

NOTES

[148] Barnes, op. cit., p. 140, and pl. 12. For an excellent representation of the "hacking" cap, see lithograph "Peytona and Fashion's Great Match," H. R. Robinson, New York, 1845, in Peters Coll., Smithsonian Institution.

[149] Macomb to Whiting, 24 Apr. 1839, LR, Cloth. Bur., tray 65, RG 92, NA.

[150] Whiting to Macomb, 17 May 1839, LS, Cloth. Bur., RG 92, NA.

[151] Two copies of this lithograph are extant: in Records of the Office, Chief of Engineers, Record Group 77 (hereinafter cited as RG 77), drawer 178–3B, Audio-Visual Branch, NA, and in CG of P, LR, tray 69, RG 92, NA. For these pattern caps see Whiting to St. John, 31 May 1839, LS, Cloth. Bur.; Irvine to Maj. Lorenzo Thomas, acting head of the Cloth. Bur., 2 July 1839, LS, CG of P; Thomas to Irvine, 5 July 1839, LS, Cloth. Bur.—all RG 92, NA. The clothing year ran from 1 Nov. to 31 Oct.

[152] Drawer 178–9, RG 77, Audio-Visual Branch, NA.

[153] L. Thomas, AAG, to Col. J. J. Abert, 7 May 1839; Abert to Officers of Corps of Topographical Engineers, 8 May 1839—both in T.E., LS, Microfilm Roll 66, RG 77, NA. The actual order, undated, is found between the entries for 8 and 9 May.

[154] Whiting to Irvine, 4 Nov. 1839, LS, Cloth. Bur.; Irvine to Whiting, 8 Nov. 1839, LS, CG of P; Whiting to Irvine, 23 Dec. 1839, LS, Cloth. Bur.—all RG 92, NA.

[155] Irvine to Ebenezer Drury, Phila., 16 Mar. 1840, LS, CG of P; contract with John T. Holloway, Phila., in Irvine to D. L. Brown, a cloth manufacturer, 16 Apr. 1840, LS, CG of P; Whiting to Col. John Walbach, 4th Arty., 18 Sept. 1839, LS, Cloth. Bur.; Whiting to Lt. Col. Alexander Fanning, 4th Arty., 9 Sept. 1840, LS, Cloth. Bur.—all RG 92, NA. The new caps were actually issued in limited quantity as early as September, probably to recruits. See Irvine to E. S. Fayssoux, MSK at Phila., 19 and 22 Sept. 1840, CG of P, LS, RG 92, NA.

[156] "Proceedings of Board of Inspectors of Clothing," 1840, MS book in USMA Library. The difference in price between the enlisted and cadet models (the latter included 34 cents profit for the storekeeper) indicates the difference in quality between officers' or cadet caps as opposed to those of enlisted men.

[157] Irvine to M. Howard, Jan.–Apr. 1841, in CG of P, LS; Irvine to W. H. Scovill, button manufacturer, 10

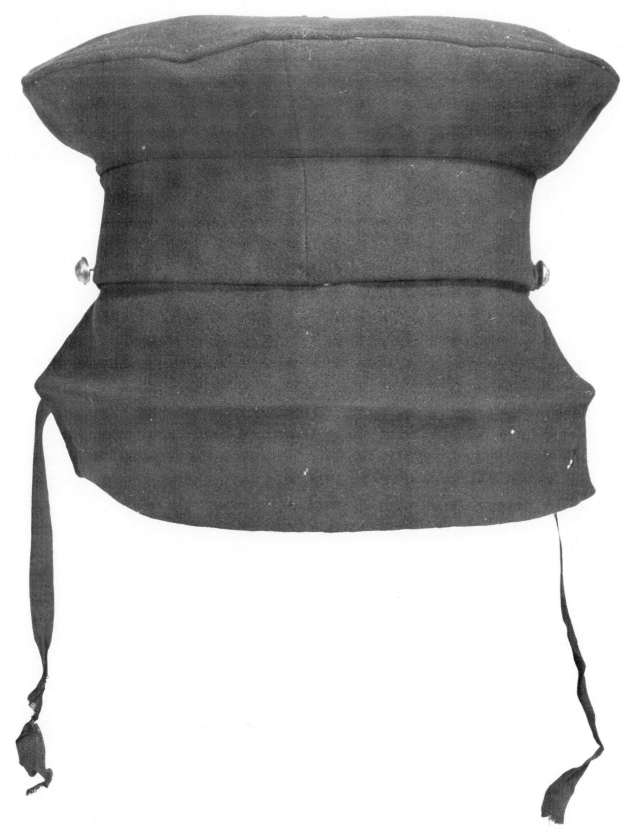

Figure 46.—Forage Cap, 1839–1851, Type 2.

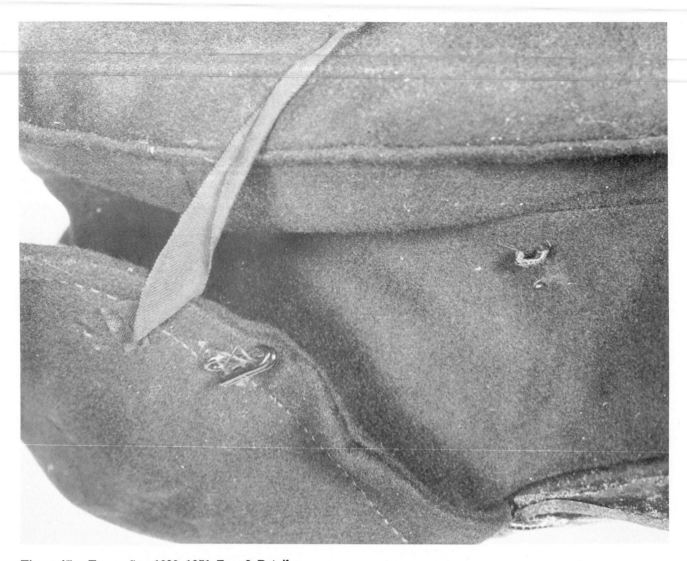

Figure 47.—Forage Cap, 1839–1851, Type 3. Detail.

May 1841, CG of P, LS; Irvine to John Gether, Cloth. Estab., 8 May 1841, CG of P, LS; John T. Holloway to Irvine, 16 June 1841, CCF (caps)—all RG 92, NA.

[158] Irvine to Brown, Phila., 16 Apr. 1840, CG of P, LS; Irvine to Brown, Phila., 11 May 1841, CG of P, LS; Irvine to Francis S. Skinner, Boston, 11 May 1841, CG of P, LS; Tyson to Wm. Phillips, 24 Dec. 1841, CG of P, LS—all RG 92, NA.

[159] Whiting to B. de la Pierce, 25 Aug. 1841, Cloth. Bur., LS, RG 92, NA.

[160] Estimate of the Quantity and Price of Materials and the Cost of Cutting and Making Clothing for the Army of the United States for the Years 1843–1846, CG of P, 2 vols. (Masterson 67), RG 92, NA. These books list in minute detail every type of material used in the manufacture of forage caps. Other records investigated—yearly price lists, contracts, etc.—also fail to mention the bands.

[161] Estimate of the Quantity and Price of Materials . . ., op. cit.

[162] Formerly belonging to Lt. James Duncan, 2d Arty., an 1834 USMA graduate. USMA collections.

[163] Order No. 26, H.Q. 1st Dragoons, Fort Leavenworth [Kansas], 31 Dec. 1846, in U.S. Army Comds., Regtl. Records, Order Book, H.Q. 1st Drags., 13 Jan. 1841–18 Apr. 1850, p. 147, RG 98, NA.

[164] *General Regulations for the Army* (Washington, 1841), p. 392.

[165] There are numerous letters concerning cadet dress between Supt. Delafield (1838–1845) and the Sec. of War in various files in the National Archives.

[166] This would make it fit either a size two or size three cap. For sizes and diameters of headgear, see, for instance, contract with H. Cressman, 23 Mar. 1843, CCF (Cressman), RG 92, NA.

[167] "Proceedings of Board of Inspectors of Clothing, Jan. 1842," MSS in USMA library. Order No. 4, H.Q. Corps of Cadets, 3 Apr. 1843, in ibid.

[168] Order No. 31, H.Q. Corps of Cadets, 7 July 1842, in ibid. The order not only forbade the removal of the stiffening but also ordered the cadets to replace it or purchase a new cap.

[169] G.O. 18, H.Q. of the Army, 4 June 1846, RG 94, NA.

[170] Uniform Board Report, 27 Apr. 1844, A.G. Doc. File B 136, 1844, Box 150, RG 94, NA.

[171] Jesup to Capt. J. B. Scott, 4th Arty., 13 Apr. 1844, Cloth. Bk., LS, RG 92, NA.

[172] There are also several period photographs of officers wearing this cap.

[173] The sewing machine is generally considered to have come into commercial use in 1850. But as late as 1861 all work at the Schuylkill Arsenal or under its supervision was done by hand, with the exception of cloth portions of caps which were machine stitched. See Capt. Roger Jones, Asst. QM to Quartermaster General M. C. Meigs, 28 June 1861, CCF (Schuylkill Arsenal), RG 92, NA.

[174] Irvine to Whiting, 7 Dec. 1839; Irvine to David Brown, Phila., 11 May 1841; Irvine to Francis Skinner, Boston, 11 May 1841—all CG of P, LS, RG 92, NA; Contract No. 31, 25 Feb. 1842, with Paul Thurlo, House Doc. 68, 27th Cong., 3rd Sess. (Serial 420).

285-667 O—69——5

☆VOLTIGEUR OR "ANDREWS" HAT, 1847☆

ONE DISTINCTIVE ITEM OF HEADGEAR was designed during the War with Mexico. Though it saw limited use and no authenticated specimen is known to exist, it is of interest as it was the prototype for a long line of campaign hats used by the Army until World War II and lately readopted for certain specialized personnel. At the start of the war Congress had leaned heavily on volunteer units with the Regular Establishment remaining unchanged. Early in 1847, however, it was found necessary to add nine regiments of infantry and one of dragoons, all regulars. Of the infantry units, eight were of the conventional type, while the ninth was organized as the Regiment of Voltigeurs and Foot Riflemen.[175]

Soon after the unit was organized, the Voltigeur commanding officer, Colonel Timothy P. Andrews, requested a felt hat for his command. As produced it was described as ". . . broad-brimmed, soft felt, of a pearl or stone color, capable of being looped up, but with a stiff brim when let down, and with an orifice for ventilation on each side of the crown that might be closed at pleasure . . . ." This hat could be folded completely flat, worn as a tricorn, as a bicorn, or could have the broad brim dropped all around to the horizontal to provide maximum protection from the sun or rain (fig. 48).[176] Approved by the Secretary of War, 500 of the pattern were procured,[177] but none reached the troops before the end of the war. In 1851 the 2d Regiment of Dragoons in Texas were issued 445 of them which had been in storage.[178] The campaign hat adopted in 1872 was based on the "Andrews" model.[179]

NOTES

[175] Callan, *Military Laws,* op. cit., Act of 11 Feb. 1847, pp. 379–382. Theoretically, half of the unit was to be mounted, each horseman being paired off with a foot soldier who was to mount and ride double when speed was needed. In practice, however, none of the Voltigeurs was mounted; the entire unit fought on foot. The regiment was inactivated after the war and never reconstituted. See John K. Mahon, "History of the Organization of the United States Infantry," *The Army Lineage Book,* vol. 2 (Washington, 1953), p. 16.

[176] *A Medical Report upon the Uniform and Clothing of the Soldiers of the U.S. Army, 15 April 1868* (Washington: Surgeon General's Office, 1868). (This is the so-called Woodhull Report, compiled under the direction of Assistant Surgeon Alfred Alexander Woodhull.) The description was determined by Woodhull after discussing the hat with Col. Andrews and others who had seen or worn it. The woodcuts reproduced were based on this information and included in the report.

[177] Col. Henry Stanton, Asst. QMG to Maj. Daniel Tompkins, QM, Phila., 10 Apr. 1847, Cloth. Bk. LS, RG 92, NA.

[178] Jesup to Col. William S. Harney, 2nd Dragoons, 26 Feb. 1851, Cloth. Bk. LS, RG 92, NA.

[179] For a full discussion of the adoption of the 1872 campaign hat, see James S. Hutchins, "The Army Campaign Hat of 1872," *Military Collector & Historian* (Fall 1964), vol. 16, No. 3, pp. 65–73.

The Andrews Hat, as generally worn.

The Andrews Hat, in the rain or excessive solar heat.

The Andrews Hat, compressed for transportation.

The Three-Cocked Hat.

Figure 48.—Voltigeur Hat, ca. 1847. From the Woodhull Report.

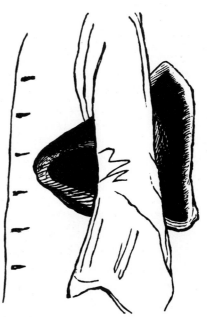

The Cocked Hat, held under the arm.

Since the adoption of the 1832 pattern dress caps and the 1832 and 1839 pattern forage caps, the Army had fought in Florida and Mexico, under widely varying climatic conditions. By 1850 the concentration of troops on frontier duty was greater than ever before. As a result of these changed conditions there was considerable desire voiced by officers and men alike for a more practical uniform for field wear to replace the tight-fitting, parade-ground dress which had been in use for so many years. Colonel Sylvester Churchill, one of the Inspectors General of the Army,[180] reported in March 1849 to the Adjutant General that he had talked to "probably more than half the officers of the Army" and the concensus was that the "full dress uniform coats, caps and hats as now worn . . . should be entirely dispensed with and substituted by the frock coat . . . . and the forage cap, with suitable plumes or pompons for full dress. . . ." They had specifically complained that the full dress cap was not "well adapted to actual service, nor indeed convenient for any service: that on campaign the . . . . forage cap [was] generally worn—always preferred. . . ." Not only were the dress items expensive and difficult to procure except in the larger cities, they further complained that in the field such items were "useless" and were stored with frequent loss or damage. Churchill himself termed the full dress cap as "high, stiff, and ponderous" and went on to state: "It is supposed that in the service likely to be performed by our foot and mounted troops, perhaps for many years, in the wilderness and Indian regions, protection of the head and body against the elements will be more important than guarding them against the sabers of well drilled dragoons."[181] He qualified these opinions only to the extent of recommending that all officers be permitted to wear the full dress as prescribed while away from troops.[182]

As a result, Secretary of War George W. Crawford,

who had received many similar complaints, directed Churchill to explore further the subject of a uniform change and to have samples prepared for his examination.[183] After a comprehensive survey and in conjunction with the Quartermaster General, the Inspector General had patterns prepared and submitted to Crawford in December.[184] Crawford approved and the uniform as recommended was made regulation in General Orders, No. 2, War Department, 13 February 1850. Paragraph I made clear the reasoning behind the change:

. . . A large number of the Officers of the Army, probably more than half, have applied since the war with Mexico, to have a uniform less expensive, less difficult to procure, and better adapted to campaign and other service. Their opinions, reasons and wishes are entitled to attention and respect; and it is important that the garments and equipments shall protect the persons of the wearers, preserve their health and make them efficient. . . .

The portions of the order pertaining to headgear were as follows:

. . . FOR OFFICERS . . . IV . . . Cap, of the material and nearly the pattern of the present forage cap worn by officers; the band or body to be three inches high, the front of which to be thickened with felt or other light material on each side of the plume stem, so as to form a groove for its reception; the visor 2¾ inches broad, reaching back to within half an inch of the tip of the ears, projecting nearly horizontal, but somewhat concave, so as to shade well the eyes and face, with oil cloth cover or case, having a flap or cape from one point of the cap visor to the other, and made to fold, double, inside of the case when not wanted for protection of the neck. The cap to be worn, without the cover, in full dress, with plumes as now used, except that those of the Dragoons will be orange color; and the Mounted Rifles, light green; those of mounted officers will rise four and those of foot officers six inches above the cap; those of the Mounted or Field Artillery, Dragoons, and Mounted Rifles, of horse-hair, falling six inches. The front ornaments, as now worn in the Staff, Staff Corps, Artillery and Infantry, with the figure, for number of regiment (three quarters of an inch long) in the angle of the cross cannon for Artillery, and within the bugle for Infantry. The Dragoons to have two cross sabres (edges upwards) instead of the star, with the number of the regiment in the angle above; the Mounted Rifles a trumpet perpendicular. A model cap for officers will be deposited at Washington, Baltimore, Philadelphia, New York, Boston, New Orleans, Cincinnati and St. Louis, as a pattern for cap makers . . . IX . . . All officers of and below the grade of Colonel, who have the brevet rank of a General officer, will wear the plume at all times of their respective departments, corps, or arm; . . . X . . . These changes in relation to officers, will go into effect on the first of October next, or before, in any regiment, or at any post, where all the officers may wish to adopt the new dress. XI . . . General Officers, on parades and reviews, and in processions, and on semi-military occasions, without troops, may wear the present full dress coats and cocked hats, or chapeaus . . . and plumes . . . . UNIFORM FOR ENLISTED MEN . . . XVII . . . Cap, of blue cloth, gig top shape; front and rear six inches high, rounded, and stiffened with felt or other light material; visor of patent leather, 2¾ inches wide, reaching back to within half an inch of the tip of the ears, projecting nearly horizontal, but somewhat concave, so as to shade well the eyes and face; on the back part a flap—outside of cloth lined with thin japanned leather—of the height of the cap, when up, for protecting the neck from sunshine and rain; front ornaments of metal, to be permanent, and to show the corps or arm; viz: Engineers, a castle; Ordnance, a shell and flame; Dragoons, two cross sabres (edges upwards), with the letter of the company in the angle above, and number of the regiment below; Mounted Rifle Regiment, a trumpet, perpendicular, with the letter of the company above; Artillery, cross cannon, with the letter of the company in the angle above and number of the regiment below; Infantry, a horn bugle with sling, with the letter of the company above and number of the regiment within the sling; all yellow, except the Infantry, which will be white. For parades or full dress, the caps will contain a pompon of wool yarn, short fringe, spherical, three inches in diameter, on a bent stem without socket, and standing forward at an angle of 45 degrees: those of Sergeants to have a crest of fringe 1½ inches above the globe; those of Engineer soldiers to be black; all others the color of coat trimmings of their respective arms; those

of all company musicians will be a netted sphere 1½ inches diameter, on a straight stem, without socket, and stiff horse-hair standing five inches high from the upper side, and spreading gently; all of the color of their corps . . . .[185]

There are several noteworthy points about these new cap forms. With the exception of making the chapeau optional on certain occasions, there was to be but one cap form for officers and one for enlisted personnel. Both caps were designed from the point of practicality to be used for both dress and fatigue or campaign duties. The "gig top shape" of the enlisted cap as mentioned in the order is difficult to define. It is clarified somewhat, however, in an undated memorandum in Churchill's handwriting dealing with the samples prepared in Philadelphia. The memo states:

The bellows tops to be higher and stiffer in front, the visor to be hollowed out more so as to conform to the shape of the head, to be larger, so as to shade the faces . . . This kind is approved because it will *fold flat*, and may be placed under a man's head . . . . Improve the forage cap by making it higher in the crown so as to contain the ornament and stiffen the top, so that it will retain a more permanent shape: for I think this will (or *should*) be the officer's cap, and the bellows top for the men. . . .[186]

From this it appears that the enlisted cap must have been very nearly a cloth version of the 1832 leather forage cap with the addition of insignia and pompons, while the officer's model seems to have been a modification of the 1839 forage cap.

General Orders, No. 25, War Department, 23 August 1850, suspended this uniform.[187] Considering the short period of time the order was in effect coupled with the large stocks of old pattern clothing left from the war with Mexico, it seems unlikely that any examples of the new enlisted cap, other than the patterns, were ever made. Some officers may have provided themselves with the new model, since the order of suspension stated that those officers who had provided themselves with the new uniform would be permitted to wear it "for the present." In any case, no examples of either form are known to exist.

A contemporary foreign comment on the 1850 uniform, and the cap in particular, is interesting, however. An editorial in the London *United Service Gazette* for 13 April 1850 praised the American Army in having ". . . . good common sense in the article of dress, and a disposition to yield to the wishes of the soldiery in adapting their costume to their personal comfort . . . . The cap—the grand difficulty with everyone but the Prussians—is, we confess, not quite to our taste, if we rightly comprehend it; but it cannot be denied that it must be peculiarly suited to a warm climate. . . ." [188]

Although these caps never came into being as items of issue, they are of importance in that they represent a trend toward practicality, simplicity, and economy which was to result in the single cap adopted the following year.

NOTES

[180] Under the provisions of the Act of 2 Mar. 1821, there were two inspectors-general in the Regular Establishment. Churchill, who served in this capacity 1841–1861, shared the office with Col. George Croghan until the latter died in 1849 and was replaced with Col. George A. McCall. At this period, the inspectors-general actively took to the field in their work.

[181] "Report on the Subject of Change of Uniform," Churchill to Adjutant General, 29 Mar. 1849, Churchill Papers, Div. of Mil. Hist., Smithsonian Inst. (hereinafter cited as Churchill Papers).

[182] Ibid.

[183] Sec. of War to Churchill, 27 Mar. 1849; Churchill to Col. Henry Stanton, Asst. Quartermaster General, 29 Nov. 1849—both in Churchill Papers.

[184] Churchill to Sec. of War, 10 Dec. 1849, Churchill Papers.

[185] G.O. 2, War Dept., 13 Feb. 1850, RG 94, NA.

[186] Undated memo, Churchill Papers.

[187] In RG 94, NA. Reasons for this suspension are unknown. Crawford's replacement by Charles W. Conrad as Secretary of War on 15 Aug. 1850, and Jesup's—long noted for his sense of economy—strong opposition to any such change until stocks left over from the late war had been exhausted, may well have been factors.

[188] Quoted in Henry I. Shaw Jr., "A British View of American Uniforms," *Military Collector & Historian* (Winter 1955), vol. 7, no. 4, p. 111.

ALTHOUGH THE 1850 UNIFORM REGULATION WITH its emphasis on simplicity was suspended before it could be put into effect, the widespread demand of the officers of the Army for a more practical uniform led to the establishment of a new Uniform Board which met early in 1851.[189] After examining the complaints that had been made regarding the old uniform as well as ". . . various collections of drawings exhibiting dress in use in Foreign Services, and having in view the character of the frontier service most likely to be required of American troops for many years to come . . ." this board submitted its report on 22 February 1851. Their recommendations were in large part approved by the Secretary of War [190] and published in General Orders, No. 31, 12 June 1851.[191] The cap and its trimmings are described as follows in the original order:

CAP

39. For all officers and enlisted men—dark blue cloth, according to pattern; crown of four upright pieces, height in front from five and three-fourths to six and one-fourth inches along the front seam; length behind, from seven and one-fourth to seven and three-fourths inches along the back seam; tip from five and one-half to six inches in diameter, and inclining downward slightly from rear to front when the cap is worn, (the dimensions given to vary with the circumference of the head;) vizor of strong neat's leather, two and one-fourth inches wide at the middle, black on the upper and green on the under sides, to be put on at right angles to the front of the cap, or in other words, to be horizontal when the cap is worn; strap of strong black leather fastening under the chin by a yellow metal buckle and leather slide; band two inches wide from the lower edge of the cap, and pointed in front according to pattern, of material, color, and with ornaments as follows:

40. For General Officers—band of dark blue velvet; with a gold embroidered wreath in front, encircling the letters U. S. in old English characters, in silver.

41. For Officers of the Adjutant General's, Inspector General's, Quartermaster's, Subsistence, Medical and Pay Departments, and the Judge Advocate of the Army—band of the same material and color as the cap, welted at the edges; the same ornament in front as for General Officers, (40.)

42. For Officers of the Corps of Engineers—the same as for the General Staff, (41,) except the ornament in front, which will be a gold embroidered wreath of laurel and palm encircling a silver turretted castle.

43. For Officers of the Corps of Topographical Engineers—the same as for the General Staff, (41,) except the ornament in front, which will be a gold embroidered wreath of oak leaves encircling a gold embroidered shield.

44. For Officers of the Ordnance Department—the same as for the General Staff, (41,) except the ornament in front, which will be a gold embroidered shell and flame.

45. For Officers of Artillery—the same as for the General Staff, (41,) except the ornament in front, which will be gold embroidered cross cannon, with the number of the regiment in silver, above their intersection.

46. For Officers of Infantry—the same as for the General Staff, (41,) except the ornament in front, which will be a gold embroidered bugle, with the number of the regiment in silver, within the bend.

47. For Officers of Riflemen—the same as for the General Staff, (41,) except the ornament in front, which will be a trumpet, perpendicular, embroidered in gold, with the number of the regiment in silver, within the bend.

48. For Officers of Dragoons—the same as for the General Staff, (41,) except the ornament in front, which will be two sabres crossed, (edges upward,) embroidered in gold, with the number of the regiment in silver, in the upper angle.

49. For enlisted men of Artillery, Infantry, Riflemen and Dragoons—bands of scarlet, light or Saxony blue, medium or emerald green, and orange-colored cloth,

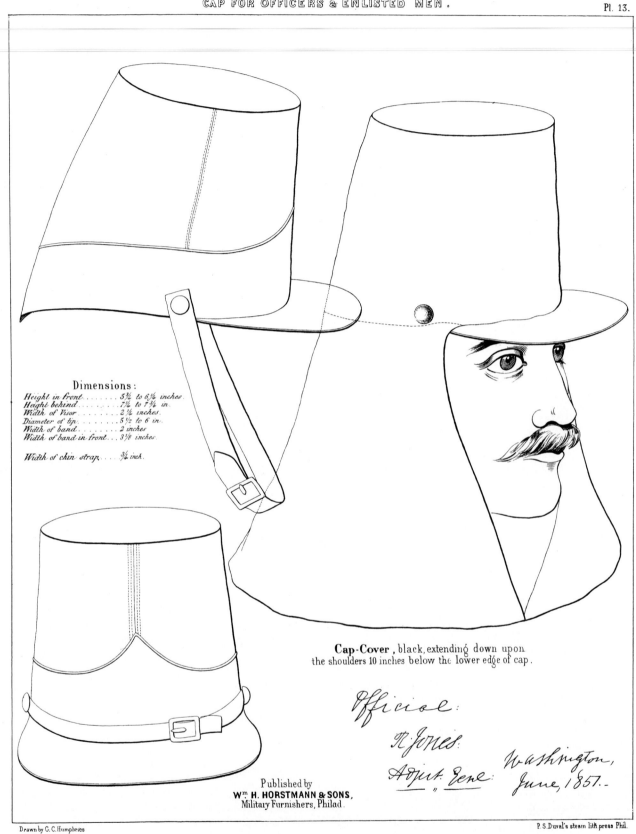

Dimensions:

Height in front........5¾ to 6⅛ inches.
Height behind........7¼ to 7¾ in.
Width of Visor........2¼ inches.
Diameter of tip........5½ to 6 in.
Width of band........2 inches
Width of band in front...3⅛ inches.

Width of chin strap.....¾ inch.

Cap-Cover, black, extending down upon the shoulders 10 inches below the lower edge of cap.

Official:

N. Jones

Adjut. Genl.

Washington,
June, 1851.

Published by
Wᵐ H. HORSTMANN & SONS,
Military Furnishers, Philad.

Drawn by C. C. Humphries

P. S. Duval's steam lith.press Phil.

Figure 49.—Cap, 1851. War Department lithograph.

respectively, with the letter of the company in front, of yellow metal one inch long. For Engineer soldiers—band of the same material and color as the cap, but edged with yellow, with a turretted castle in yellow metal, in front. For enlisted men of Ordnance—band of the same material and color as the cap, but edged with crimson; a shell and flame in yellow metal, in front.

CAP COVER

50. For officers and men—(to be worn in bad weather) black, of suitable water proof material, with a cape extending below the cap ten inches, coming well forward, and tying under the chin; according to pattern.

POMPON

51. The pompon will be worn by all officers whenever the epaulettes are worn, and by the enlisted men, on all duty under arms; except when the cap cover, (50,) is put on.

52. For General Officers—a gold embroidered net acorn, three inches long, with a gold embroidered spread eagle, one and three-fourths inches between the tips of the wings, and so attached to the base of the pompon as to show in front of the cap below its top.

53. For all other officers, and for all enlisted men—spherical, two and one-fourth inches in diameter, and as follows:

FOR COMMISSIONED OFFICERS

54. Of worsted, permanently attached at the base to a gold netted circular ring two-thirds of an inch in diameter, by one-third deep, with gold embroidered spread eagle, as for General Officers, (52,) and of the following colors:

55. For the Adjutant General's Department—lower two-thirds buff, upper third white.

56. For the Inspector General's Department—lower two-thirds buff, upper third scarlet.

57. For the Judge Advocate—white.

58. For the Quartermaster's Department—lower two-thirds buff, upper third light or Saxony blue.

59. For the Subsistence Department—lower two-thirds buff, upper third royal or ultra marine blue.

60. For the Medical Department—lower two-thirds buff, upper third medium or emerald green.

61. For the Pay Department—lower two-thirds buff, upper third dark olive green.

62. For the Corps of Engineers and Topographical Engineers—lower two-thirds buff, upper third black.

63. For the Ordnance Department—lower two-thirds buff, upper third crimson.

64. For the Artillery—scarlet.

65. For the Infantry—light or Saxony blue.

66. For the Riflemen—medium or emerald green.

67. For the Dragoons—orange.

68. For Aids-de-camp—buff.

69. For Adjutants of Regiments—same as for the Adjutant General's Department, (55.)

70. For Regimental Quartermasters—same as for the Quartermaster's Department, (58.)

FOR ENLISTED MEN

71. Permanently attached at the base to a yellow metal circular ring, two-thirds of an inch in diameter, by one-third deep, with yellow metal spread eagle, one and three-fourths inches between the tips of the wings, and so attached to the base of the pompon as to show in front of the cap below its top; according to pattern; and of the following colors: for Artillery, scarlet—Infantry, light or Saxony blue—Riflemen, medium or emerald green—Dragoons, orange—Engineers, yellow—Ordnance, crimson.[192]

Of particular interest in the cap trimmings and insignia was the change in the facings: the infantry from white to blue, in the interest of practicality, the rifles from black and yellow to green—a reversion to the traditional—and the dragoons from yellow to orange with the substitution of crossed sabers for the sunburst and eagle.

Although the basic cap is clearly described above, actual specimens (figs. 50–52) reveal additional details. The inner body of the cap was initially of a cardboard-like material made of felted cotton and rabbit fur. The crown, or side portion, of the body was of one piece with the top of the same material glued to it. The dark blue wool outer portion, with the top stitched to it with a narrow welt of the same material showing at the seam, was slipped over this body. A sweatband of either glazed muslin or thin leather was stitched to the outer surface of the cap and turned under, giving a welt-like appearance. The black patent leather visor, measuring $2\frac{1}{2}$ inches at its widest point and 8 to 9 inches from side to side depending on the size of the cap, was flat with rounded corners, tapering rather deeply to the rear, and not always green on its underside as prescribed. The two-piece black leather chin strap terminated at either end in buttons of the appropriate service and had a brass tongued buckle and single keeper stitched to the right portion of the strap. Around the base of the cap was the prescribed cloth band, in the color of the branch of service, $1\frac{3}{4}$ inches high in back, gradually rising in height around the sides until it came to a point $3\frac{1}{2}$ inches above the center of the visor. The band was hemmed at top and

Figure 50.—Cap, 1851.

bottom and basted to the cloth crown. The engineer "soldiers" and ordnance enlisted personnel, unlike the other crops, had cap bands in the color of the cap with a ⅛ inch welt at the top and bottom of the band in the color of their respective corps. At the top front of the caps were two stitched eyelets, one above the other, for the insertion of the pompon and pompon eagle holders.

All of these caps, unlike the dress caps of the earlier periods, were manufactured at or under the direct supervision of the Clothing Establishment at Schuylkill Arsenal. This was apparently the result of the problems experienced with outside contractors in producing the 1839 forage cap and the Arsenal's own later success with it. Although some specimens examined bear only a size number, many carry the label pasted inside the

top: "No./size: [ranged from 1 to 5]/United States/ (Schuylkill) Arsenal." All the leather components for the cap and the insignia were contracted for separately and assembled on a piecework basis. In December 1853 the Assistant Quartermaster at Philadelphia reported that 26,672 of the new pattern caps had been made there since June 1851.[193]

The only officer's cap examined was one that belonged to William Tecumseh Sherman when a captain in the Substance Department in 1851–1853. It follows the basic enlisted pattern, with the officer's cap band as prescribed, but is of finer material and better workmanship than those produced at the Arsenal. It bears the trademark, "SMITH, CRANE & CO./NO. 4 MAIDEN-LANE/NEW YORK," is gilt inside the

Figure 51.—Cap, 1851.

top and lined with black cotton. The sweatband of brown leather, fitted with drawstrings, is stitched inside the cap body with no welt around the outer lower surface.[194]

It is of interest in regard to the manufacture of these caps that in 1851 the Army purchased its first sewing machines for use at the Arsenal.[195] Despite initial glowing reports on the machines,[196] and extensive experimentation on both caps and clothing, the innovation was not considered a success, the personnel of the Arsenal feeling that while perhaps practical for "the requirements of populous and civilized life" they were not "the answer for the hard wear and tear . . . of our

frontier service." As a result, use of the machines was continued only for those elements of the uniform "not exposed to much hard usage."[197] Actually, few of the caps examined show evidence of any but hand sewing except for the colored cap bands, which for the most part are machined hemmed top and bottom.

The cost of this new headgear was $1.17 for the basic cap and $1.73¾ for the cap complete with insignia, cover, band, and pompon. Engineers, who had a more elaborate cap device, paid slightly more. The basic cost of the 1832 cap was $1.13 ($1.15 for the 1833 dragoon model). With all insignia and trim the price ranged from $2.32 for the noncommissioned

Figure 52.—Cap, 1851.

graceful in looks than the 1832-1833 models. It was lower, measuring some 6¼ inches in front as opposed to the former height of 7½ inches. The spherical pompon was only 2¼ inches in diameter, a great change from the former plumes that in some cases towered as much as 12½ inches over the already tall cap. As mentioned earlier, the 1832 cap was the first of a series based on French rather than British styles. The 1851 model continued to reflect this influence: it was almost an exact copy of the form adopted by the French in 1844.[200] Serving a dual purpose, this cap was a compromise, and like most compromises was not a complete success. Though lower and lighter than the old pattern, it was not as light or as practical for active duty as the forage cap, which sat almost flush with the head. The waterproof cover, however, which fitted over the cap and extended down over the neck and ears was a distinct improvement.

Reactions to the new cap varied. One extreme reflecting the traditionalist point of view of some officers was vividly expressed in a cartoon drawn by Lieutenant George Derby of the Topographical Engineers under the pseudonym of John Phoenix (fig. 53).[201] This reaction was hardly universal, however, for one periodical commented: "We think changes in dress are important . . . and as to the caps as heretofore worn they were disgraceful. The style of cap now adopted approaches very nearly that of the French and some other European Armies. . . ."[202] In 1854 Inspector General Churchill reported that since June 1853 at nine posts he had inspected, 14 officers approved of the new pattern while 36 disliked it; 14 officers also approved of the new pompons while 36 preferred short plumes; and only one of the officers who disliked the cap was able to offer a better solution.[203] The commanding officer of the 1st Dragoons, then at Fort Union, New Mexico, requested for his unit a reversion to the 1839 forage cap. He wrote the Adjutant General in Washington:

> The present uniform cap, however ornamental it may be, or however suitable for the other Corps of the Army, is entirely unsuitable for the Dragoon service, being heavy, heating and painful to the head when used in the sun, wind, or at a rapid gait. It incommodes the Dragoon in the use of his arms, in the management of his horse when mounted and in the care of his horse in the stable, as well as in all fatigue duties.[204]

In 1854 the colored cap band of the enlisted men of the line was replaced by a band of the same dark blue

staff of dragoons to $1.42¾ for an infantry private. The cost of the 1839 forage cap was 81¼ cents in 1848.[198] Based on the old issue rate of two dress caps and one forage cap for each five year enlistment, it cost the government $3.07¼ to furnish an infantry private with all his old pattern headgear for one enlistment exclusive of trim and insignia. The 1851 cap was to be issued at the rate of seven for each five year enlistment, or a total of $8.19 plus insignia and trim. The goal of simplicity had been achieved, but not that of economy. The cap was issued as early as September 1851 by the recruiting service.[199]

The adoption of this cap form was a distinct improvement in several respects. There was but one form of headgear for officers and enlisted personnel. It varied only in quality and was authorized to serve for full dress, dress, fatigue, and campaign duties. This answered the long-standing complaints of the officers and also eased the strain on their pocketbooks. The new cap, with its forward sloping crown giving a rather rakish appearance, was certainly more colorful and

THE NEW UNIFORM

This cartoon satirizes the ridiculous tall cap which in 1852 superseded the cocked hat.

Figure 53.—"John Phoenix" on the 1851 Cap. From "John Phoenix, Esquire, The Veritable Squibob" by George R. Stewart, Jr. Copyright 1937 by Henry Holt and Co. Copyright © 1965 by George R. Stewart, Jr. Reproduced by permission of Holt, Rinehart and Winston, Inc.

material as the cap itself, with a welt of the color of the arm or service of the wearer stitched to the upper edge (fig. 54). At the same time, the colored facing on the collar and cuffs of the enlisted frock coat were similarly replaced.[205] The reason for these changes is unknown, but examination of a number of cap bands and uniform coats in the national collections reveals a wide range of fading of colors, which would certainly have given an unsightly appearance to troops on parade. One small additional change: the 1851 cap band of the engineer and ordnance troops, of the same blue cloth as the cap body, carried a colored welt at the top and

Figure 54.—Cap, 1854.

bottom of the band; in the 1854 version the lower welt was eliminated.

Rather than a felted cap body, several caps of the basic 1851–1854 pattern in the collections have a body of white cloth vulcanized on both sides of a gutta-percha base, stitched together in the rear with the top separately applied, and all carrying in the crown the trademark "VULCANIZED GUTTA PERCHA/ MADE BY/NORTH AMERICAN/GUTTA PERCHA/COMPANY/RIDER'S & MURPHY'S/ 1852 & 1854/PATENT" stamped in a red circle. At the top of the body on all four sides are ventilation holes about ¼ inch in diameter. These bodies represent a series of experiments in the early 1850s in which a number of articles made of gutta-percha were submitted to the Army for trial. Gutta-percha is a substance somewhat similar to rubber taken from the sap of the Isonandra or Gutta tree found in the Far East. John Rider and John Murphy perfected and patented a process whereby this material could be vulcanized and made capable of use in a wide variety of pieces of clothing and equipment.[206] In view of the publicity given this new substance and upon the recommendation of the Quartermaster General, the Secretary of War ordered a board of officers convened to review the subject. The board reported favorably and a number of examples of clothing and equipment including a cap body were sent to the field for extended tests.[207] There is record of some officers expressing a preference for this cap body, stating that it was less liable to be crushed than the felted body and stood up better in rainy weather,[208] but a check of contracts after 1855 reveals none with the North American Gutta Percha Co., so it can be assumed that the material was dropped for use by the Army.

Although the 1851 cap was designed to serve both for dress and fatigue use, the stocks of the 1839 pattern forage cap were so large that they were not exhausted until March 1855, thus many of the troops had both a dress and a fatigue cap until that date.[209] In August 1855 a campaign hat was prescribed for the personnel of the newly organized 1st and 2d Cavalry Regiments to serve for both dress and fatigue.[210] In March 1858 a campaign hat replaced the cap for all branches of service, and in November 1858 a new style forage cap was authorized.[211] As a final blow to the 1851 pattern, the Quartermaster General directed in April 1859 that all caps of the 1851 pattern be issued as forage caps.[212] The style was not forgotten however,

for the dress cap of the new uniform prescribed in 1872 proved to be an abbreviated version of the same basic pattern.

NOTES

[189] G.O. 40, War Dept., 31 Dec. 1850, RG 94, NA.

[190] Bvt. Lt. Col. Joseph H. Eaton to AG, 28 Apr. 1851, contains the report of the Uniform Board. See also AG to Maj. Gen. Winfield Scott, 22 May 1851—both in AGO File U.12, 1851, RG 94, NA.

[191] In RG 94, NA. These regulations were also privately published as *Regulations for the Uniform & Dress of the Army of the United States, June 1851, from the Original Text and Drawings in the War Department* (Philadelphia: William H. Horstmann and Sons). This edition quotes the general order verbatim, but its greatest value is the 25 plates in black and white and color of the uniform and accessories. The originals of these drawings have never been located.

[192] Ibid., pp. 6–7.

[193] Maj. George H. Crosman to Jesup, 29 Dec. and 30 Dec. 1853, Office of Army Clothing and Equipage (hereinafter cited as O of AC & E), LS, RG 92, NA.

[194] Sherman Collection, U.S. National Museum Accession 59388.

[195] Deputy QMG Charles Thomas to Sec. Of War, 26 June 1851, QMG Reports, vol. 1, LS, RG 92, NA. These machines were among the first invented and patented by Isaac Singer in 1851. (Singer had sold a number of them before he received his patent.) The patent model of this machine in the collections of the U.S. National Museum carries the serial number 22.

[196] See Crosman to Jesup, 17 Apr. 1851, LS, O of AC & E, RG 92, NA.

[197] Jesup to Hebrand and Co., New Orleans, 31 Mar. 1859, LS, OQMG, Clothing, RG 92, NA. The principal difficulty experienced with all early sewing machines was the maintenance of proper thread tension.

[198] G.O. No. 1, H.Q. of the Army, 2 Jan. 1851, RG 94, NA; G.O. No. 64, War Dept., 29 Nov. 1848, RG 94, NA. 1848 has been chosen as the year during the period least likely to reflect any undue fluctuation of the currency. The price of any newly adopted item was always higher the first year or so of its procurement.

[199] Crosman to Jesup, 8 Sept. 1851, O of AC & E, LS, RG 92, NA.

[200] J. Margerand, "Les coiffures de l'armée: les coiffures de l'infanterie de 1815 á 1900," *Revue Mensuelle Illustrée* (Paris, June 1911), p. 30.

[201] George R. Stewart, *John Phoenix, Esquire, the Veritable Squibob, A Life of Captain George H. Derby* (New York, 1937), pp. 79–80.

[202] *Gleason's Pictorial*, Boston (22 May 1852), vol. 2, no. 21, pp. 328–29.

[203] Churchill to Sec. of War Jefferson Davis, 27 Feb. 1854, AGO File No. B136, 1844, RG 94, NA.

[204] Col. T. T. Fauntleroy to Col. S. Cooper, 30 Oct. 1854, in US Army Comds, H.Q., 1st Dragoons, LS, 25 Oct. 1849–9 Oct. 1863, RG 98, NA.

[205] G.O. 1, War Dept., 20 Jan. 1854, RG 94, NA.

[206] *Gutta Percha: Its Discovery, Properties, Manufacture, & C. With an Illustrated and Descriptive Catalogue of Vulcanized Gutta Percha Fabrics, Manufactured under the Patents of Rider and Murphy, by the North American Gutta Percha Company, and for Sale at their Warehouse, 102 Broadway and No. 1 Pine Street, New York* (New York, 1854), in CCF (Gutta Percha), RG 92, NA.

[207] "Proceedings of a Board of Officers to Examine Gutta Percha," 21 Apr. 1855, CCF (Gutta Percha), RG 92, NA.

[208] Col. George Wright, 9th Inf., to Adj. Gen., 13 Sept. 1855, CCF (Gutta Percha), RG 92, NA.

[209] Jesup to Maj. Crosman, 12 Mar. 1855, LS, Cloth. Bk., RG 92, NA.

[210] G.O. 13, War Dept., 15 Aug. 1855, RG 94, NA.

[211] G.O. 3, War Dept., 24 Mar. 1858; G.O. No. 13, War Dept., 30 Nov. 1858—both in RG 94, NA.

[212] Jesup to Commanding Officer, Fort Laramie [Wyoming], LS, Cloth. Bk., RG 92, NA.

APPENDIX: MAKERS OF HEADGEAR

THE ATTACHED ALPHABETICAL LISTING contains the names of the firms which were awarded contracts to make headgear by the War Department during the period 1808 through 1851. As of 1808, Congress required the Secretary of War to furnish a complete listing of all contracts his office made with civilian firms during each calendar year. This information was published in House or Senate documents. No attempt has been made to list the lengthy titles of each individual document since they can be readily located under the heading "Army Contracts" for the appropriate year in Ben. Poore's *A Descriptive Catalogue of Government Publications of the United States, September 5, 1774—March 4, 1881* (Senate Misc. Doc. No. 67, 48th Cong., 2d Sess.) (Washington: Government Printing Office, 1885).

The listing of a firm's name here is not proof that it actually produced headgear, for it is known that some suppliers did not fulfill their contracts and the Army had to have other firms produce the items. Probably in over 90 percent of the cases, however, these names do represent actual makers. It is also known that some of the purveyors and later assistant quartermasters did not report the name of the contractor but only listed the amount of money expended and the number of items procured. Again, this amounts to a very minute segment of the total number procured during the years concerned. It should also be noted that these contracts represent suppliers of headgear for enlisted men only. Officers procured their clothing independently from a maker of their choice.

Aurand, Peter, Reading, Pennsylvania
1809—engineer hats, 25

Aurand, Peter and John Lotz, Reading, Pennsylvania
1808—infantry hats, 5,000
1810—artillery cocked hats, 1,550
    artillery hats, 1,600
    engineer hats, 20

1812—light artillery caps, 800
    infantry caps, 12,200
    chapeaux, 500
    artillery hats, 500

Boas, John, Reading, Pennsylvania
1812—infantry caps, 1,000

Bushar, Charles
1812—infantry caps, 2,000

Coles, Thomas
1812—infantry caps, 6,800

Cressman, Henry, Philadelphia, Pennsylvania
1814—infantry leather caps, 1,500
    artillery leather caps, 500
    dragoon caps, 246
1819—leather caps, 4,000
1821—leather caps, 1,000
1822—leather caps, 1,900
1825—leather caps, 800
1826—leather caps, 2,700
1827—leather caps, 1,500
1828—leather caps, 1,000
1830—leather caps, 4,000
1831—leather caps, 1,800
1833—uniform caps, 5,000
1834—uniform caps, 225
1835—uniform caps, artillery and infantry, 1,509
    uniform caps, dragoon, 118
1836—uniform caps, dragoon, 715
1843—uniform caps, infantry, 2,000
    uniform caps, dragoon, 400

Cressman, William, Philadelphia, Pennsylvania
1838—uniform caps, infantry and artillery, 1,500
    uniform caps, dragoon, 500
1840—uniform caps, infantry and artillery, 4,000
    uniform caps, dragoon, 400
1841—uniform caps, infantry and artillery, 1,000
    uniform caps, dragoon, 300

285–667 O—69——6

1843—uniform caps, infantry and artillery, 1,000
1845—uniform caps, infantry and artillery, 3,050
    uniform caps, dragoon, 650

Crocker, Perey
1813—infantry caps, 300

Dallam, Samuel
1808—rifle caps, 800
1813—infantry leather caps, 1,000

Dickenson, Frederick and Charles
1812—chapeaux, 1,500
    infantry caps, 4,000

Dickinson, Josiah and Sons, Northampton, Massachusetts
1811—artillery hats, 1,140

Dillingham, Edward
1813—infantry caps, 200

Dingee, Robert, New York
1814—leather caps, infantry, 15,000
    leather caps, artillery, 1,200
1818—leather caps, 2,299
    felt caps, 501
1819—felt caps, 60
    leather caps, 546
1821—leather caps, 1,000

Disler, Jacob
1814—leather caps, infantry, 10,000
    leather caps, artillery, 4,000

Domett, George, Boston, Massachusetts
1833—uniform caps, 1,000 (all rejected)

Drury, Ebenezer
1840—forage caps, 7,500

Eustis, Jacob
1812—infantry caps, 3,500

Flomerfelt, George, Philadelphia, Pennsylvania
1816—leather caps for heavy artillery, 2,000
    leather caps for riflemen, 200
1817—leather caps, 3,200

Foering, Abraham P.
1813—infantry leather caps, 1,000
1814—leather caps, dragoon, 241

Forgave, William
1813—leather caps, infantry, 500
1814—leather caps, infantry, 1,500
    leather caps, artillery or rifle, 1,500

Freeman and Miller
1812—infantry caps, 1,000

Gansevoort and Legrange
1812—infantry caps, 1,500

Gibbs, Joel
1812—infantry caps, 1,200

Gilder, Ruben
1813—leather caps, infantry, 1,000

Gilman, Joseph S.
1812—infantry caps, 1,000

Gratucap, H. T., New York (this should be Gratacap)
1846—uniform caps, infantry, 8,000
    uniform caps, dragoon, 1,000

Green, Joseph
1812—infantry caps, 500

Green, Joseph and Jacob
1812—infantry caps, 3,000

Hahle, William
1808—infantry hats, 4,200

Haines, John, Philadelphia, Pennsylvania
1808—light artillery caps, 760
    rifle caps, 665
    light dragoon caps, 430

Halsey, Silas
1812—infantry caps, 1,000

Hansell and Braentigam, Philadelphia, Pennsylvania
1813—dragoon caps, 50
    leather caps, infantry, 1,000

Harlow, Joshua
1813—infantry caps, 450

Hathaway and Snyder
1837—uniform caps, infantry and artillery, 2,000
    uniform caps, dragoon, 540

Hendrick, Luther B.
1812—infantry caps, 800

Hill, James M.
1836—forage caps, infantry and artillery, 3,000
    forage caps, dragoon, 500
1837—forage caps, infantry and artillery, 1,400
    forage caps, dragoon, 1,615

Hill, William
1837—forage caps, infantry, 900
    forage caps, dragoon, 1,466
1838—forage caps, infantry, 3,084
    forage caps, dragoon, 1,074

Holloway, John T.
1833—forage caps, infantry and artillery, 5,204
1834—forage caps, 225

1837—forage caps, infantry and artillery, 2,000
  forage caps, dragoon, 1,200
1840—forage caps, 7,500

Howard, M.
1841—forage caps, infantry, artillery, and dragoon, 10,000 (this contract was not completed)

Johnson, John
1813—cavalry helmets, 50

Kendrick, Walter
1811—felt wool caps, 2,500

Kerr, James
1811—caps, rifles, 602
  caps, light artillery, 587
  caps, dragoon, 690
1812—caps, dragoon, 1,200
1813—leather caps, infantry, 1,500

Kinsey, Edmund
1808—leather caps, light artillery, 760

Knower, Benjamin
1813—infantry caps, 2,500

Langdon, John Jr.
1812—infantry caps, 2,000

Leavitt, Samuel
1813—infantry caps, 2,500

Lee, Adam and Henry R.
1811—felt wool caps, 3,065

Lukens, Jonathan, Philadelphia, Pennsylvania
1808—leather caps, 800
1812—dragoon caps, 500
1813—leather caps, infantry, 1,000
1814—leather caps, infantry, 1,000
  leather caps, artillery, 1,000

Lyons, Mathew, Philadelphia, Pennsylvania
1812—dragoon caps, 300

Marr, George
1813—leather caps, infantry, 500

Martin, Robert C.
1812—dragoon caps, 700

Mather, Nevins and others
1812—infantry caps, 5,000

Post, C. H.
1846—uniform caps, dragoon, 1,000

Plummer, John H.
1812—infantry caps, 1,000

Primrose, John
1812—dragoon caps, 300
1813—leather caps, infantry, 1,000

Primrose, Violet
1813—leather caps, infantry, 500

Raymond, Charles F., Philadelphia
1834—uniform caps, artillery, infantry, and dragoon, 1,225
1835—forage caps, artillery, and infantry, 2,800
  forage caps, dragoon, 200
1836—uniform caps, artillery and infantry, 3,000
  uniform caps, dragoon, 400

Redfern, Robert, Philadelphia, Pennsylvania
1819—leather caps, 5,000
1821—leather caps, 1,000
1822—leather caps, 1,000

Richards, George
1812—artillery hats, 192

Rowland, S. and A. Kurtz
1808—hats, infantry, 1,000
  hats, artillery, 500

Russell, A. & Co.
1833—uniform caps, dragoon, 715

Russell, Samuel
1812—infantry caps, 1,000

Seawards, Nathaniel
1813—caps, infantry, 300
  caps, artillery, 200

Sheets, Conrad
1808—hats, infantry, 500
  hats, artillery, 300

Schultz, Frederick
1813—leather caps, infantry, 1,000

Smith & Brown, Philadelphia, Pennsylvania
1833—forage caps, dragoon, 800
1834—forage caps, 1,400

Smith, Christian B.
1812—chapeaux, 100

Smith, Ernest C., Philadelphia, Pennsylvania
1844—uniform caps, infantry, 3,600
  uniform caps, dragoon, 400
1845—uniform caps, dragoon, 300

Smith, G. R.
1842—uniform caps, infantry, 1,000
  uniform caps, dragoon, 300

Stahle, William
1808—hats, infantry, 250
  hats, artillery, 300
1812—chapeaux, 300
  infantry caps, 70

Stroup, George
    1812—infantry caps, 500

Thomas, Thomas L. & Son
    1813—infantry caps, 500

Tieber, George
    1812—yeoman crown hats, 1,000
           infantry caps, 1,000

Trainor, James
    1818—leather caps, 816

Vose, E. & J.
    1813—caps, infantry, 1,000
           caps, artillery, 500

Walker, James
    1812—dragoon caps, 200
    1813—leather caps, infantry, 1,000
    1814—dragoon caps, 202

Way, George
    1813—leather caps, infantry, 500

Welch, John
    1813—leather caps, infantry, 1,000

Weller, Benjamin
    1812—infantry caps, 1,500

Wolcott, Alexander
    1812—infantry caps, 2,500

Woodward, Joseph C.
    1818—leather caps, 300

BIBLIOGRAPHY

MOST OF THE DOCUMENTARY MATERIAL for this volume was found in the files of the various branches of the War Department which are on deposit in the National Archives, Washington, D.C. The majority of this material is in Record Group 92, which bears the somewhat misleading title of Records of the Office of the Quartermaster General.

The responsibility for the procurement or manufacture and issue of military clothing did not fall under the Quartermaster General until 1842. From 1800 to 1812 it was under the Purveyor of Public Supplies and from 1812 to 1842 under the Commissary General of Purchases. The records of both of these officers are filed with Record Group 92. Both maintained letter books which contained copies of all letters sent, eight volumes for the first office and eighteen for the second. Letters received by both offices are filed in some 140 boxes entitled the "Coxe-Irvine" papers. Unfortunately, they are not always filed by date of document and the box titles do not adequately reflect the contents.

In 1832 the Clothing Bureau was established as a separate office directly under the Secretary of War to supervise the clothing operations of the Commissary General of Purchases. The letter books of this office, which cover the entire period of its existence to 1841, are also in Record Group 92. This block is extremely helpful in that it contains all of the decisions of the Secretary of War on matters of uniform. Unfortunately, the letters received are intermingled with the afore-mentioned "Coxe-Irvine" papers and are difficult to locate for the entire period.

The Office of the Commissary General of Purchases was eliminated in 1842 and its function of procurement, storage, and issuance of army clothing was transferred to the Office of the Quartermaster General. A separate set of books of letters sent concerning clothing was set up as well as a register of letters received. The latter are split in two blocks, one set arranged by the file reference in the register, which contains a very small proportion of the material; the other, which comprises the bulk of this correspondence, is integrated in an overall block of letters received by the Quartermaster General's Office as a whole, a total of 1,275 boxes and is entitled the "Consolidated Correspondence File." These letters are arranged by the name of the sender, the office of origin, or by subject. The choice of subject is often obscure.

Also in Record Group 92 are some pertinent files from various offices at the Philadelphia Depot (also termed the Schuylkill Arsenal), which was the largest single permanent storage depot as well as the principal factory and procurement office for enlisted men's clothing. Among these records are the letters sent by the Assistant Quartermaster General at Philadelphia, who had overall charge of all functions of the Depot after 1842. Initially, his letters sent were a continuation of the letter books of the Commissary General of Purchases. Later, they were filed as letters sent by the Office of Army Clothing and Equipage. There is also a set of registers of letters received by this office, but the letters themselves are not always readily located—some were incorporated with the "Coxe-Irvine" papers, others were forwarded to Washington and eventually incorporated in the Consolidated Correspondence File, and some lost or destroyed. The Military Storekeeper at Philadelphia had been responsible since 1801 for the storage and issue of all material made or procured. The files of that office which have been most valuable are the "Journal" (Masterson 115), consisting of nine volumes, covering the period 1801–1842, and the the "Journal" (Masterson 115), consisting of nine from 1805 to 1813. Both categories contain a chronological record which includes nomenclature, quantity, and price of all articles received in and issued from the stores, together with the name of contractor or receiving unit.

As every change in the uniform of the Army had to be approved by the Secretary of War, records of his office maintained in Record Group 107 are of value. This Group contains his letters sent to the Quartermaster General and preceding officers and registers of incoming letters which contain a synopsis of the contents as well as action taken and where the letters were sent.

Record Group 94, Records of the Adjutant General's Office, contains all of the orders that formally authorized specific changes in uniforms and frequently contains the reports of boards convened to discuss such changes. The letters-sent volumes contain additional information on the decisions of the Secretary of War on interpretation of existing orders or minor matters not deemed worthy of an individual order.

In certain cases the chiefs of branches of the Army maintained very complete files on changes in the uniforms of their particular service. Record Group 77, Records of the Chief of the Corps of Engineers, letters sent and received, contains correspondence and drawings of the chapeau of that corps. Also in Record Group 77 are the records of the Corps of Topographical Engineers, which contain a fairly complete file of letters sent and received on the chapeau and forage cap adopted in 1839.

BARNES, ROBERT MONEY. *A History of the Regiments & Uniforms of the British Army.* London: Seeley Service & Co., Ltd., n.d.

CALLAN, JOHN F. *The Military Laws of the United States, Relating to the Army, Volunteers, Militia, and to Bounty Lands and Pensions, from the Foundation of the Government to the Year 1863, To Which are Prefixed the Constitution of the United States, (With an Index Thereto,) and a Synopsis of the Military Legislation of Congress During the Revolutionary War.* Philadelphia: George W. Childs, 1863.

CAMPBELL, J. DUNCAN, and HOWELL, EDGAR M. *American Military Insignia 1800–1851* (U.S. National Museum Bulletin 235). Washington: Smithsonian Institution, 1963.

CARMAN, W. Y. *British Military Uniforms from Contemporary Pictures, Henry VII to the Present Day.* London: Leonard Hill (Books), Ltd., 1957.

CATTLEY, ALEX. R. "The British Infantry Shako," *Journal of the Society for Army Historical Research* (London) (Winter 1936), vol. 15, no. 60, pp. 188–208.

DE PEYSTER, JOHN WATTS. *Personal and Military History of Philip Kearny, Major-General, United States Volunteers.* New York: Rice and Gage, 1869.

ELTING, JOHN R., and McBARRON, H. CHARLES, JR., "3rd Regiment, United States Artillery, 1812," *Military Collector & Historian.* (Summer 1964), vol. 16, no. 2., p. 48.

FINKE, DETMAR H., and TODD, FREDERICK P. "French Influence on Early Uniforms of the United-States Army," *Revue Historique de L'Armée* (1957), special issue entitled Fraternité D'Armes Franco-Américaine, pp. 46–51.

HEITMAN, FRANCIS BERNARD. *Historical Register and Dictionary of the United States Army from Its Organization September 29, 1789 to March 2, 1903.* 2 vols. Washington: Government Printing Office, 1903.

HICKS, JAMES E. *United States Ordnance, vol. 2 Ordnance Correspondence.* Mt. Vernon, N.Y.: James E. Hicks, 1940.

HUTCHINS, JAMES H. "The Army Campaign Hat of 1872," *Military Collector & Historian* (Fall 1964), vol. 16, no. 3, pp. 65–73.

JOHNSON, DAVID FUNSTON. *Uniform Buttons, American Armed Forces 1784–1948.* 2 vols, Watkins Glen, N.Y.: Century House, 1948.

KNOETEL, HERBERT, and SIEG, HERBERT. *Handbuch der Uniformkunde, die militarische Tracht in ihrer Entwicklung bis zur Gegenwart.* 3rd ed. Hamburg, Germany: Helmut Gerhard Schulz, 1937.

KOKE, RICHARD J. "The Britons Who Fought on the Canadian Frontier, Uniforms of the War of 1812," *The New-York Historical Society Quarterly* (April 1961), vol. 45, no. 2, pp. 141–194.

LAWSON, CECIL C. P. *A History of the Uniforms of the British Army.* vol. 1, New York: A. S. Barnes & Co., Inc., 1940 (reprint 1962); vol. 2, London: Peter Davies, 1941; vol. 3, London: Nicholas Vane, Ltd., 1961.

LEWIS, WAVERLY P. *U.S. Military Headgear 1770–1880.* Devon, Conn: printed by author, 1960.

McBARRON, HUGH CHARLES, JR. "American Military Dress in the War of 1812—III Regular Infantry," *Journal of the American Military Institute* (Fall 1940), vol. 4, no. 3, pp. 184–196.

McCLELLAN, E. N. *Uniforms of the American Marines, 1775–1827 (mimeograph).* Washington: Marine Corps Historical Section, Department of the Navy, 1932.

MALIBRAN, H. *Album du guide à l'usage des artistes et des costumiers publié en 1904 contenant la description des uniformes de l'armée française de 1780 à 1848.* Paris: Boivin & Cie, 1907.

MALIBRAN, H. *Guide à l'usage des artistes et des costumiers contenant la description des uniformes de l'armée française de 1780 à 1848.* Paris: Combet & Cie, 1904.

MARGERAND, J. "Les coiffures de l'armée française," series appearing 1909–1924 in *Revue Mensuelle Illustrée* (Paris).

Military Collector & Historian—Journal of the Company of Military Historians (1949–1965), vols. 1–17.

"New Regulation Uniform of the United States," *Gleason's Pictorial* (Boston) (May 22, 1852), vol. 2, no. 21, pp. 328–329.

North American Gutta Percha Company. *Gutta Percha: Its Discovery, Properties, Manufacture, & C. With an Illustrated and Descriptive Catalogue of Vulcanized Gutta Percha Fabrics, Manufactured under the Patents of Rider and Murphy, by the North American Gutta Percha Company, and for Sale at Their Warehouse, 102 Broadway and No. 1 Pine Street, New York.* New York: Narine & Co. Printers, 1854.

PARKYN, H. G. *Shoulder-Belt Plates and Buttons.* Aldershot, Great Britain: Gale & Polden, Ltd., 1956.

PRUCHA, FRANCIS PAUL, ed. *Army Life on the Western Frontier, Selections from the Official Reports Made Between 1826 and 1845 by Colonel George Croghan.* Norman, Oklahoma: University of Oklahoma Press, 1958.

RISCH, ERNA. *Quartermaster Support of the Army; A History of the Corps 1775–1939.* Washington: Government Printing Office, 1962.

RODENBOUGH, THEOPHILUS FRANCIS. *From Everglade to Canon with the Second Dragoons . . . 1836–1875.* New York: D. Van Nostrand, 1875.

ROGERS, H. C. B. *The Mounted Troops of the British Army 1066–1945.* London: Seeley Service & Co., Ltd., 1959.

SHAW, HENRY I., JR. "A British View of American Uniforms," *Military Collector & Historian* (Winter 1955), vol. 7, no. 4, p. 111.

SPAULDING, OLIVER LYMAN. *The United States Army in War and Peace.* New York: G. P. Putnam's Sons, 1937.

STEWART, GEORGE R. *John Phoenix, Esquire, the Veritable Squibob, a Life of Captain George H. Derby, U.S.A.* New York: Henry Holt & Co., 1937.

TODD, FREDERICK P. "The Leather Forage Cap at West Point," *Military Collector & Historian* (June 1954), vol. 6, no. 2, pp. 38–40.

TRANSFELDT, WALTER, and FRHR. V. BRAND, KARL-HERMANN. *Wort und Brauchtum des Soldaten, Geschichtliche und sprachliche Betrachtungen uber Gebrauche, Begriffe und Bezeichnung des deutschen Heeres in Vergangenheit und Gegenwart.* 5th ed. Hamburg, Germany: Helmut Gerhard Schulz, 1959.

U.S. Adjutant and Inspector General's Office. *Articles of War, Military Laws and Rules and Regulations for the Army of the United States, September 1816, revised 1817.* E. de Krafft, n.d.

U.S. Adjutant and Inspector General's Offices. *Military Laws, Rules and Regulations for the Army of the United States . . . September, 1816.* E. de Krafft, printer, n.d.

U.S. Congress. *American State Papers, Class V. Military Affairs.* 7 vols. Washington: Gales and Seaton, 1832–1861.

U.S. Department of the Army (Department of Defense). *The Army Lineage Book, Volume II, Infantry.* Washington: Government Printing Office, 1953.

U.S. Military Magazine 1839–1842, vols. 1–3.

U.S. National Gallery of Art. *The Civil War, A Centennial Exhibition of Eyewitness Drawings.* Washington: National Gallery of Art, 1961.

U.S. War Department. *General Regulations for the Army; or, Military Institutes.* Philadelphia: M. Carey & Sons, 1821.

U.S. War Department. *General Regulations for the Army; or, Military Institutes.* Washington: Davis & Force, printers, 1825.

U.S. War Department. *General Regulations for the Army.* Washington: Francis P. Blair, printer, 1834.

U.S. War Department. *General Regulations for the Army of the United States; also the Rules and Articles of War, and Extracts from Laws Relating to Them.* Washington: Globe, printers, 1835.

U.S. War Department. *General Regulations for the Army of the United States, 1841.* Washington: J. and G. S. Gideon, printers, 1841.

U.S. War Department. *Regulations for the Uniform & Dress of the Army of the United States, June 1851, from Original Text and Drawings in the War Department.* Philadelphia: William H. Horstmann and Sons, 1851.

Welsh, Peter C. *Tanning in the United States to 1850, A Brief History* (U.S. National Museum Bulletin 242). Washington: Smithsonian Institution, 1964.

WOODHULL, ALFRED ALEXANDER. *A Medical Report upon the Uniform and Clothing of the Soldiers of the U.S. Army.* Washington: Surgeon General's Office, 1868.

75

U.S. GOVERNMENT PRINTING OFFICE: 1969 O—285-667